JAMES RANDI

PSYCHIC

INVESTIGATOR

JAMES RANDI:

PSYCHIC

INVESTIGATOR

First published in the UK by
Boxtree Limited
36 Tavistock Street
London WC2E 7PB

Published in association with Granada Television and Open Media

Designed by Sarah Hall
Cover design by Paterson-Jones
Cover photographs by Stewart Darby/Granada Television

Typset by Bookworm Typesetting, Manchester

Printed and bound in Great Britain

A CIP catalogue entry for this book
is available from the British Library

ISBN 1-85283-144-8

CONTENTS

**THOSE WHO BELIEVE WITHOUT REASON
CANNOT BE CONVINCED BY REASON**

DEDICATION

This book is dedicated to Michael Hutchinson. I've known him since my early days as a Britophile, and he has patiently guided me through the many cultural confrontations and differences I've encountered. Over the years he has been a willing assistant and a very valued colleague to whom I have never turned in vain for information, advice or any other sort of support, and I cherish his continued participation in my life and in my work. He has patiently endured my inconsistencies and ignored my weaknesses, and has scolded me only when absolutely necessary.

Though some may see Michael and me as latter-day versions of Don Quixote and Sancho, I prefer to think of us as colleagues in a sometimes thankless but often satisfying battle against prejudice, irrationality and misinformation.

Alas, I see yet another windmill ahead. Michael, good friend, to horse!

ACKNOWLEDGEMENTS

I thank Sebastian Cody, executive producer of Open Media, for his heretical belief that we could actually put a whole string of psychics and others through a test procedure and also make it into good TV. Producer Frankie Glass gave me a smile or a hug when I most needed one, while fencing with me over scripts and schedules, never flagging in her determination, enthusiasm and good will. Director John Birkin exerted only gentle persuasion to squeeze from the process whatever beauty was possible and make it all presentable. The impressive patience of floor manager Ian Galley was tried to the fullest extent by a presenter who could never manage to find the series of taped 'marks' so carefully laid down for him.

Researchers David Britland, Louise Clover and Susan Walls daily flattened their ears calling hordes of psychic performers, all of whom claimed different and sometimes surprising psychic gifts. Designer Liz Ashard created a studio set of crystals, pyramids and smoke that took the viewer to Looking-Glass Land in one stroke, and Angela Murgatroyd turned out endless versions of scripts that I managed to mangle for her while she provided spiritual consolation and chastisement to me from on high in the control room, a very special place inhabited by semi-mythical beings.

At the eye of this perpetual storm, Pamela Wylde dispensed advice, paper clips, cash and wisdom, and even survived the sarcasm of the cab driver who could hardly believe that he'd been summoned to drive the party of 'Wylde and Randi'. Perhaps he was disappointed.

Gilles-Maurice de Schryver helped me through two shows, and we are both grateful for the hospitality of the Order of the Magi in Manchester, who cheered me on. The home fires were tended by José Alvarez and Matt Patterson while I was away in the wilds of Manchester beguiling the public.

Dr Steven Donnelly attended the taping sessions in Manchester, and shared his valuable observations with me. That assistance is gratefully recognized.

Finally, Sue Blackmore and John Maddox kindly consented to add their considerable prestige to our efforts.

To one and all, my very sincere thanks.

James Randi
Plantation, Florida
2 April 1991

THE RETURN OF LEWIS CARROLL

We begin our journey behind
the looking-glass.

Three variations on dowsing-stick use are shown in this French book of 1783,
Superstitions de Tous les Peuples.

CHAPTER 1

THE RETURN OF LEWIS CARROLL

An ill judged plan is not only profitless,
but also leads men to destruction.
Phaedrus, 8 BC-AD 71

The series of six programmes presented by Granada in 1991, titled *James Randi: Psychic Investigator*, was not my first experience in that genre. Back in 1983 a major US TV network ran a special that was called, over my strenuous objections, *Magic or Miracle?* as if there were a difference between the two phenomena. That programme was governed by the feeble-minded notion that the audience didn't really want to be informed either way, and absolutely unsupported statements were presented to support theories of the paranormal.

As a professional conjuror, I found that I was being asked by professional reporters and writers for my opinions on various purportedly paranormal events, and I began to incorporate a lecture into my performance. At present I make most of my income from a straight lecture and demonstration entitled *Science and the Chimera*, dealing with the problems experienced by scientists who have no expertise in methods of trickery and the problem of self-deception. As a co-founder of the Committee for Scientific Investigation of Claims of the Paranormal (CSICOP), I am active in their projects and I have been called in on many serious investigations of doubtful scientific claims, such as the 'magnetic sensing' tests done at Manchester University, 'spoon bending' by children at the University of Bath, and research performed in France by Dr Jacques Benveniste on the subject of homoeopathy.

It was a considerable improvement when my 1989 investigatory TV 'special' programme, also made in the USA, was called *Exploring Psychic Powers: Live!* The producers of this programme, who were – perhaps understandably – very nervous about the outcome, had no knowledge of statistics nor of probability. They had put up $90,000 of the $100,000 prize which was offered for proof of a paranormal phenomenon. I supplied the remainder, in accordance with an offer I had made some time previously and which still stands (see Appendix).

The producers were worried about the tests that the seven contestants were to perform, since the company had a lot to lose – but they were reassured by the two scientists we had asked to assist us in the design and implementation of the tests, who pointed out that the likelihood of any claimant obtaining the prize by chance alone was vanishingly small.

Those two scientists were Drs Ray Hyman and Stanley Krippner, the latter a distinguished past president of the Parapsychological Association and still a very active parapsychologist. Ray Hyman is a psychologist with the University of Oregon at Eugene, and is recognized as a leading authority on parapsychology and statistical analysis.

From the start the US TV special ran into problems. I had tried to make the tests as fair and rigorous as possible. The producers, however, feared that it would be hugely unentertaining to watch all the psychics go down in flames and, to my dismay, two performers were booked to appear on the programme to give demonstrations of their specialities without any attempts being made to subject their methods to controls. That might have been expected to give some small hope to the watching believers. But in the event, all the claimants failed to demonstrate any psychic powers whatever – after which one of the two entertainers offered another TV audience the opinion that those who had actually been tested weren't real psychics at all, but only actors. I felt inclined to agree with him, but not in the way he meant.

The present series
Early in 1990 I was approached by Open Media, who had produced several interview and investigatory programmes that had attracted my interest. We formulated the idea of a TV series that would look into various claims of paranormal, occult and supernatural events. From the very first meetings the producers and I held on the subject, it was determined that our series would not offer the claimants any sort of platform from which they could merely advertise their wares, unless they also agreed to be properly, fairly and precisely tested, and this was written into the contract.

To obtain subjects Open Media took advertisements in *Psychic News*, a London-based newspaper with a wide circulation and which offers very uncritical acceptance of all matters that appear to be supernatural. This publication, and the expected word-of-mouth activity, brought an avalanche of mail to us. Some of it was useless for our purpose, since it consisted of scribbled notes from raving loonies. The majority, however, came from people who, we felt, were honestly convinced of their psychic abilities. We also posted specific invitations to a number of celebrated psychic performers who had come to our attention through the press or who often appeared on television doing just the kind of thing that we wanted to test.

The people we chose
In considering the qualifications of possible participants for our program-

mes, we looked at their reputations and their claims. Most of those we believed acceptable had excellent standing in the psychic hierarchy, and they offered us an incredible spectrum of wild claims. Some told us that they regularly served large corporations or celebrities in an advisory capacity or in a more material manner. Cancer cures, flying lessons (I mean without an aeroplane!), mind-reading, discovering buried treasure, predicting the stock market and diagnosing and curing ailments were only a few of the wonders we were offered. Unfortunately we found that in most of the more interesting applications we pursued the claimants were too shy, or unable, to produce actual demonstrations, or were subject to negative vibrations, or unwilling for some other reason to show us their wares.

One applicant sent us a long list of predicted events that he was sure would appear in the newspapers on certain dates. Although we subsequently failed to match a single actual event with any of these prophecies, even being exceedingly generous with interpretations, he railed at us for refusing him airtime. We discovered that he was one of those people who constantly call the newspapers about their predictions. Letting such people on to the programme might well have given us a reputation for only including somewhat unbalanced applicants, though that accusation was made anyway after the various claimants failed to deliver. It was a case of 'Why did they choose her? I know I could have done it!'

It should be noted that many of those who declined our offer, especially the mailed invitations, were and are full-time professionals who advertise regularly and who make a living from their work. We were surprised that they had chosen not to share their talents with us, especially since all were to be paid regular fees for their participation, as was everyone who appeared.

What is science, anyway?

Science is, quite simply, a search for knowledge of the universe around us. We observe, we draw conclusions from those observations, we design experiments to examine those conclusions, and we end up stating a theory which should express a new fact or idea. But, if new or better evidence comes along, we must either discard our theory or amend it to accommodate that evidence.

Scientists aren't always right. And they don't always follow the rules exactly. The monk Gregor Mendel, performing his experiments in the mid-1880s which established the fundamental laws of heredity, apparently altered his figures slightly so that the results were somewhat more convincing – but in the long run, despite this 'honest' fiddling with his data, he was right. The fact that other researchers can, even today, replicate his experiments and thus validate his conclusions has provided us with firmly established scientific laws about heredity. Galileo, Kepler, Newton,

Einstein, Curie and hundreds of other men and women of science may have made some errors along the way, but they provided us with knowledge that has made our lives richer, fuller and more productive.

And what is parapsychology?

Among all the sciences there is one known as parapsychology. It studies certain reported events, such as extrasensory perception (ESP), psychokinesis (moving objects by mental power), divining and prophecy, that have no presently known explanation. Like all other sciences, it develops theories to explain these claimed events, and attempts to test those theories by experiment. However, unlike those made in other sciences, none of the parapsychologists' experiments have both shown positive results and been replicated by independent researchers. The *Guinness Book of Records*, attempting to list the most astonishing performance in ESP, could only report that the episode fails to meet its standards. Data in some important basic parapsychological experiments that yielded apparently positive results have been shown to be falsified – though parapsychology is far from alone in this respect.

Paranormal phenomena have to be examined rationally. If they cannot be, studies of them should be consigned to the dustbin along with the flat-Earth theory, Father Christmas and perpetual-motion machines, none of which can have the slightest importance to anyone except, perhaps, students of abnormal psychology or editors of the tabloid press.

The rules of our programmes

When we talked to the people who applied to participate about their being definitively tested, we heard much more protest than agreement. We were determined from the start to avoid simply providing a showcase for them, and would not test them unless they told us that they were confident of success and approved 100 per cent of the protocol we developed with them. Therefore any who had doubts about the genuineness of their claimed powers might have been expected to refuse to participate.

If some favourite miracle worker did not show up in our series, it was not because he or she was not invited. That person might not, of course, have heard of our offer. Yet considering the advertising that we did, and the great number of personal invitations to well known psychics that we sent out, it would be a minor miracle in itself if they failed at least to be aware of it.

Our intentions

It was our hope that this series of programmes might change some minds about the way paranormal, supernatural or occult claims are often evaluated. We wanted to offer our viewers a series of carefully designed tests with selected persons who claimed to have these abilities. Obviously, we could not contend that our tests would prove or disprove the existence of psychic or other unusual powers; the amount of data we could present was plainly insufficient for that. Rather, we intended to cover each subject by giving the public a body of evidence from which they could draw their own conclusions.

We made it clear that no person who appeared and failed to perform as claimed could be fairly said not to have those powers he or she professed; but, if any of our claimants were successful to a significant degree, those powers might well appear to be genuine, and further tests would certainly be called for. As far as possible, we encouraged those who were tested to return for another set of tests if they so desired.

I have found that believers frequently say of such tests that they were 'not properly done' – when the results turn out to be negative. It was our hope that the audience would not find that to be so with our programmes. We asked those who professed expertise in these subjects for suggestions as to how we might improve our protocols, and in so far as those suggestions were acceptable to our scientific advisors, we tried to adopt them.

The advisors

In order to give as much validity as possible to the programmes, we invited two prominent professional parapsychologists in the UK to participate in the design of the experiments. Both declined. However, we were fortunate to have parapsychologist Dr Susan Blackmore, and Dr John Maddox, editor of the leading scientific journal *Nature*, present to offer advice and criticism.

Hard to test

Selecting persons to be tested for our series of programmes was far from easy. Many of those who applied turned out not to be testable. Since any idea, theory or claim which has been clearly stated is testable, a word of explanation is needed here. We asked all claimants to make a simple statement of what they believed they could do. This, apparently, was beyond some of them. We got responses such as 'I get impressions about people' or 'I help people get better.' Such answers were hardly enough for us to develop a proper, satisfactory method of examining the claims of these people.

For example, a few applicants sent us samples of what they called 'psychic portraits' – drawings of dead persons. In every case they told us that the only evidence they had that the persons so represented had ever lived was the acceptance of the 'sitters' for whom the images were produced (a matter we will discuss in a moment), and they were unable to produce a likeness of any specific person on request. It can be seen that belief in their abilities to conjure up images from beyond death was exceedingly doubtful, and not susceptible of proper examination.

But what of the fact, so often encountered, that a sitter will accept a likeness as representing someone they have known? First, these performances are usually done before a very large audience, and all present are challenged to come up with a correspondence between the portrait and someone – anyone – who looked even vaguely like the drawing; they are pressured into acceptance.

Second, it seemed to us from our interviews with several sitters that they had, perhaps unwittingly, 'gone along' with the artist in order not to cause any conflict. They were, after all, believers, and they wanted the performance to succeed and to be a positive experience.

Third, and most important, the subjects of such experiences, when they reconstruct the conditions later, are often the very worst judges of whether or not something marvellous really occurred. This last fact has been established thoroughly by researchers, and it is particularly evident to experienced conjurors. In fact, in Chapter 4 we will find an excellent example of this phenomenon in which a subject tried to recall accurately what was told him during a 'reading'.

Even when *Psychic News* reported the results of our studio taping sessions, they got it seriously wrong. Figures, facts and names were garbled. If simple evidence like that cannot be correctly reported, what can we expect of accounts of more subtle aspects of the events?

A firm agreement

Whenever a claim was made to us that appeared to be testable within our means, we agreed to do a test and made it quite clear that the test would take place exactly as outlined in the mutually agreed manner which had been decided on beforehand. A few who agreed to these rules decided nevertheless to back out at the last minute. That meant that we would only be testing persons whom we had every reason to accept as sincere and honest.

However, sincerity is not enough evidence for anyone to accept a claim, especially if it is not likely, by usual standards, to be true. For example, from my personal experience I have found that dowsers, those who believe they can find water, minerals or other objects or substances by means of a forked stick, a pendulum or other simple instrument, seem always absolutely and honestly convinced of their abilities. That conviction is not well founded, since the majority of properly performed, comprehensive tests of this particular claim have produced negative results.

I must add, having mentioned dowsing, that on only two occasions during the many years I have been testing psychic or supernatural claims have I found a dishonest dowser. They are, generally speaking, upright, sincere people; occasionally a little pompous as well, but that's not a serious fault. Usually, though, one needs something more tangible to be pompous about.

A minor mythology

You will hear the lesser media chortling over the discovery that 'I once said that I am a liar, a cheat and a fake.' I have said that more than once. In fact I use that expression every time I step on stage, whether as a conjuror or as a lecturer. It's my way of telling my audience, straight up front, that I'm an actor who plays the part of a magician. Yes, I use deception to accomplish my impersonation. In the same way that any actor achieves a part, I employ make-up, costume, scripts, delivery and design to produce an illusion. But, unlike most actors, I may also employ certain secret bits of sleight of hand, applications of technology and sensory misdirection to perform successfully. Though an audience assumes deception by an actor, it may not make that assumption when witnessing a conjuring performance. As Paul Daniels or David Copperfield will tell you, there are some out there beyond the footlights who actually believe that these gentlemen perform miracles. They do, almost. But not quite.

Briefly, and without wishing to appear paranoid, I should also tell you that in the past few years there has been a genuine campaign to discredit me and my work. Unable to deny the contents of my books and articles on paranormal subjects, a small group of misguided believers and frustrated practitioners of spurious miracles has concocted a bizarre tale of my life of which H.P. Lovecraft (or Ian Fleming) would have been quite proud. No, I am not an employee of the American CIA, nor am I a communist. I have not been arrested for 'inciting riots', nor for 'civil disobedience'. I was not deported from the USA as an undesirable person, I am not involved with narcotics and I do not accept the multitude of other nefarious attributes assigned to me by my opponents – though I cannot predict what new and diverting transgressions they will summon up with which to burden me. Fables come, as they say, with the territory.

Granada Television, in advance of my signing contracts with them, were sent a letter outlining most of the dire failings listed above. Happily, they saw through it and reacted accordingly. I signed contracts the next day.

For the record

It is a fact that no paranormal, psychic or supernatural claim has ever been substantiated by proper testing. It's not enough merely to gather huge amounts of anecdotal material in support of these avowed powers, and correct testing methods are not always seen to be so. For that reason we attempted in our programmes, wherever possible, to supply the reasons for our procedures.

On each programme I demonstrated an admitted trick or two in which viewers might, if not informed to the contrary, find proof that I had psychic abilities. I assured them that I did not possess such powers, and that those tricks were accomplished by quite ordinary means. We knew that some viewers, because they seem not able to admit that they are not capable of solving such matters, might choose to assume that I do have magical powers. We assured everyone that to do so would be an error of judgement.

In several instances guests we had invited to be present so that they might freely express their opinions suddenly abandoned those opinions when the cameras turned to them, and we were left without that information to convey to our viewers. A few of those guests, disturbed by the frequent failure of the psychics to perform as expected, took the studio floor and harangued us for ten minutes, unable to understand that their contribution would have to be cut down to a minute or so to leave time for the rest of the programme.

Many of those who initially agreed to appear suddenly changed their minds and cancelled. This practice is rather unpopular with TV producers and presenters, especially when hours have gone into preparing a detailed script that is rendered useless by such a capricious event. Fortunately there were claimants who were able to fill in at short notice, and we were grateful to them for their co-operation.

A strange world indeed

I warned the researchers who became involved in this project that they were stepping through the looking-glass when they began interviewing people for the series. They soon found that I had told them the truth. Most of those who claim to have paranormal powers seem to live in a special world. Their abilities, they say, cannot be examined by regular means that would be considered acceptable in any other discipline. They develop their own jargon to describe their unique gifts, much of it borrowed from scientific terminology and stealing validity by that appropriation. They sometimes disagree with one another so markedly that only one of them can be right, and all may be wrong. Logic, rational thought and plain common sense are tools they avoid using lest their ideas fail to pass even cursory examination. Most importantly, they insist that their tenets can be properly examined only by persons who believe them – in advance of any examination – and who do not hold any sceptical views on the subject.

After handling the many strange requirements of these claimants, and eliminating most of them because they could not agree to the very simplest of controls, we began taping the programmes in March 1991.

It was an adventure.

THE CRYSTAL SET

How a 50p crystal is transformed
into a £25 panacea through imagination,
misinformation and marketing.

CHAPTER 2

THE CRYSTAL SET

*Any man may commit a mistake, but none but
a fool will continue in it.*
Cicero, 106-43 BC

A few years ago I was in New York City to play a bit part in a film. Sharing
the scene with me was Andy Warhol, the pop artist who rose to fame
through his ability to sell rich people paintings of Campbell's Soup cans.
Off camera, we got into a conversation about New Age notions, then a
relatively new kind of mystical flummery and beginning to be fashionable.
He informed me that he depended on amethyst crystals to preserve his life,
opening his shirt to display a mass of violet gems held in gold chains
forming a literal vest of hardware. 'Without this, I'd probably be dead!' Mr
Warhol told me. And he described to me the subtleties of 'crystal power'
that had so far kept him alive.

Only a few weeks after that Andy Warhol died on an operating table from
complications following a surgical procedure. I'm sure that his gem vest
was removed at that time, and inevitably I was led to wonder if perhaps he'd
had a valid point.

Mr Warhol's enchantment with the subject was understandable. We have
all been fascinated by the wonderful organization and symmetry of crystals.
Even common salt assumes square shapes when it is given the opportunity,
and more esoteric substances produce intricate forms; these are signs of the
arrangement of their atoms. Water, in the form of snowflakes, is one of the
most beautiful examples of the phenomenon.

True to form, the mystics have taken up this expression of nature as
further proof of their claims, and they now ascribe to crystals various
powers of healing, influences that will bring financial gain, precognitive
ability and other unlikely potentials. They point to recognized attributes of
crystals, long used by science and technology, as support for their own
notions. One of these is the piezoelectric effect, which simply means that
when certain crystals such as quartz are squeezed, a small electrical signal
is given out; and that when, conversely, an electrical signal is applied to
the crystal, it expands or contracts in response. It can be made to vibrate at
a certain frequency, in the same way as a bell sounds a particular note

when it is struck. There is nothing at all mysterious about this phenomenon, but it serves the theories that amateurs publish in New Age literature, asserting that crystals give out some sort of vibrations that psychics can detect.

In shops that cater to the need for supernatural guidance and benefits, one can now pay fifty times the former price for what was once only an attractive addition to a mineral collection, but is now touted as a magical remedy for many problems and afflictions, as well as a key to infinite wisdom and power.

The crystal claimant

We hear endlessly of these mythical powerful vibrations so, as part of our coverage on *James Randi: Psychic Investigator*, we wanted to test a psychic's ability to sense such forces. One of those whom we invited to be tested was Soozie Holbeche, who has written a book on the alleged paranormal properties of gems and crystals, and is well known in the field. Soozie told us that she would be able to pick out one crystal among many which would have particularly strong values for a given individual. In other words, this would be a 'good' crystal with beneficial effects for this specific person.

We asked Fiona Richmond, the prominent TV personality and journalist, to assist us on the programme in which we handled this subject, and Soozie set about finding a crystal among her collection which was especially 'tuned' to Fiona. It turned out to be a small, clear quartz crystal.

A dubious technique

Now, this crystal chosen by Ms Holbeche was obviously supposed to be 'special', and I asked her to demonstrate how she had decided that it was identified with Ms Richmond. She used, she told us, a New Age technique called 'applied kinesiology', also known simply as AK. This variety of New Age claptrap has been tested endlessly, and always found useless, as discussed in *The Skeptical Inquirer*. It consists of having the subject stand with a test substance in one hand, while the other arm is stretched straight out from the side. The operator places a hand on the outstretched arm and presses down with a certain force, attempting to push the arm down and judging the degree of that force. This is compared with the amount of force needed to depress the arm when the test substance is not being held by the subject in the other hand, or when a 'bad' substance is held.

It is claimed that when a harmful substance is being held, the arm depresses easily; when a 'good' substance is present, the force needed is much greater, since the crystal strengthens the bearer.

I may say that I first came upon AK when my foster son, Alexis, reported to me that his dentist had used it on him to show that sugar was a detrimental substance. The dentist had placed a sugar cube in Alexis's hand and pressed down the other arm more easily than when no sugar cube was held. When we visited the dentist so that I might witness this wonder, he assured me that even the word 'sugar' written on a bit of paper would produce the same effect. Apparently I had taught Alexis well in the art of scepticism, for when the dentist exulted that the test had been positive, Alexis revealed that he'd switched the sugar cube for a similar cube of styrofoam! The dentist, not at all confounded, merely observed that this test obviously indicated that styrofoam was also bad for the teeth, and declined to proceed with the bit-of-paper test. We were dismissed from his office as people 'with the wrong attitude'. I changed dentists. I somehow suspected that he had a fault with his own attitude. In the USA, incredibly, courses are offered to dentists in which AK is taught.

Two birds with one stone

Obviously, with Soozie Holbeche's planned procedure, we found that we were now in a position to examine two major New Age claims in one test. In fact Soozie told us confidently that even if we only wrote a negative word ('dead', 'war') on a scrap of paper, and placed that paper in the subject's hand, applied kinesiology would show a dramatically different result from when a positive word ('alive,' 'peace') was used! However, since we were specifically interested in testing the claims made for crystals, we decided only to test a crystal.

I told our audience that Ms Holbeche had agreed to tell us which among five small bags contained the chosen 'good' crystal, while the other four held a control substance. Would she be able to detect it reliably? She assured us that she would.

Now, I don't question for a moment that Soozie Holbeche honestly believed - and, I'm sure, still believes – that she is really able to detect a crystal by means of its 'vibrations' and by applied kinesiology. But, in similar tests, when the subject of the experiment does not know whether his or her arm should be weaker under pressure, and the operator does not know whether the result should be positive or negative, the experimenters have always failed to get other than chance results.

We used a simple randomization technique to mix up the five bags, and they were all placed in a larger black bag. The chance of being able to find the correct item by guessing alone was one in five, or 20 per cent. But Soozie had said that she'd be finding it from its 'good vibrations' compared with the 'bad' vibrations of the other control substances, which we told her were very 'bad' materials indeed. She was not working, so she claimed, just by chance, and since she had demonstrated that she was able to detect the crystal with 100 per cent accuracy when she knew where it was, she should now have been able to achieve that same accuracy.

Since this was ther test, we allowed her all the time she needed for the process. No one, not myself nor our audience, knew at this point in which bag the crystal was.

Soozie Holbeche pumped away at Fiona Richmond's arm, testing each of the five bags as Fiona selected them from the larger bag. Soozie then chose one bag which, she said, contained the 'good' crystal.

That little bag turned out to contain a lump of rat poison, so unless Ms Richmond is lacking a dietary supplement known as strychnine, Soozie Holbeche was, on that occasion at least, unsuccessful in locating the 'good' vibrations. In repeated tests her results were exactly in accordance with chance.

What is the New Age?

Since both applied kinesiology and crystal power are what are known as 'New Age' developments, I must clear up one thing: the New Age psychic phenomenon is not new. It is simply a collection of 'Old Age' fads, from spiritualism to faith-healing, that has had a few seconds in a microwave oven to warm it up. Rather than sitting in a dark room holding clammy hands with total strangers of unknown worth, followers of New Age leaders such as Shirley MacLaine now sit in a fully lit auditorium in $600 seats — beside strangers of unknown worth.

As we might expect, there are religious zealots who have identified New Age notions with Satanism and general godlessness. That's going a bit far. Some fundamentalists in the USA have belaboured the police and the media with claims that children have been sacrificed to Satan by his worshippers. However, investigator Shawn Carlson, an astrophysicist at the Lawrence Berkeley Laboratory in Berkeley, California, looked into these allegations and concluded that though there were no documented sacrifices of children, there were more than 2,000 children beaten to death by their parents in the USA in the year 1988. Surely that indicates a misapplication of righteous zeal.

New Age devotees, in my view, are just silly, immature people poking about for the secrets of the universe in the ashes of their dreams and finding terrors at every turn to threaten their blissful ignorance.

Auras — the haloes of the New Age saints

A New Age claim that has received a great deal of attention is that humans are surrounded by some sort of glow that is invisible to all but gifted psychics. This 'aura' is of variable size, quality and colour, according to the aura seers, and those variables are indications of character, emotions and even health.

The Irish charm of aura reader James Garvey was not lost on our audience when he appeared on *James Randi: Psychic Investigator*. Mr

Garvey told us that he would be able to detect auras through solid walls and even over the telephone; but since the latter does not make good television, we decided to test his ability to identify auras of five studio audience members when they stood behind a translucent screen.

The five volunteers stood behind a screen which had been divided into five sections labelled A, B, C, D and E, lit from behind so as to cast their shadows sharply on to the screen. James Garvey did not know which volunteer stood behind which section. He told us that, besides the shadows, he could clearly see their auras as well, right through the screen. At that point the light was switched off, and I called out, at random, one of the volunteers' names and asked them to step out from behind the screen. Mr Garvey's task was to use his claimed powers of aura perception to state from which position, A, B, C, D, or E, the volunteer had come.

The volunteer was then asked to take up whichever position Mr Garvey thought he or she had occupied, the only difference being that the volunteer now stood in front of the screen and not behind it.

One by one the volunteers were called from behind the screen and Mr Garvey allocated them positions in front of it. The laws of probability entail that the chances of Mr Garvey placing each volunteer before the correct section of the screen were 1 in 120. Alas, at the moment of truth, only two of our subjects were found to be in their right places. On this occasion at least, James Garvey had not demonstrated that he was really seeing auras.

THE MAGIC WAND

Sticks, rods and pendulums.

CHAPTER 3

THE MAGIC WAND

*It does not become men to pay indiscriminate respect
to every kind of divination.*
Pythagoras, 586-497 BC

Dowsing, also known as divining, has been around for a long time. In common with any idea that boasts great antiquity – like the flat-Earth theory and astrology – it is embraced by wishful thinkers who believe that age is equivalent to value. It is first described in print in Agricola's 1540 Latin book on mining, *De re metallica*, published at Basle in Switzerland.

The process can take many forms. The traditional method is to grasp a flexible green forked stick (hazel and willow are preferred) so that the main stem points straight away from the body, and the forks are held one in each hand, palms up and the elbows tightly against the body. The resulting strained position of the hands forces the forks apart. This, as with all other methods of dowsing, provides a system which is in very unstable equilibrium, since the tendency is for the stick to whip up or down unless care is taken to balance it. There is thus potential energy stored in the system, and the slightest inclination or relaxation of either hand will result in the stick moving violently. This motion is taken as evidence that there is an external force acting upon the device.

Another popular method uses two straight, stiff wires about 24 inches (60 cm) long, each bent sharply at one end at a right angle to provide a handle which is held vertically in the fist so that the main portion is pointing straight ahead and parallel to the ground. The object is to hold the two rods parallel to one another, and the dowsing 'reaction' is said to occur when the rods diverge or when they cross, depending upon which dowser you listen to. Again, the tiniest inclination of the hand can cause great fluctuations in this system. Sometimes only one rod is employed.

Incidentally, dowsers sometimes disagree completely. I have seen instructions that tell learners never to try dowsing when wearing rubber boots, while others insist that it helps immeasurably. Some practitioners say that when rods cross, that's a sign of water; others say that water makes the rods diverge to point opposite ways. Many say that the metal rods are not suitable at all for dowsing.

An illustration from Agricola's 1540 book *De re metallica* shows a dowser
working with a forked stick to discover minerals.

Pendulums are also frequently used. A weight of any kind is suspended
at the end of a string or chain. Crystals, real or fake, are currently the rage.
Various movements of the bob are interpreted in different ways by different
dowsers. In this method, it can always be seen that the operator moves his
hand to set the pendulum swinging, though he will vehemently deny that he
does so. To-and-fro motions and circles are produced, often in answer to
questions directed by the dowser at the pendulum. Yes, the operator speaks
to the pendulum!

Though these are the principal devices used, individual operators come
up with a fantastic array of others, including exotic variations on the
standard ones. Single flexible 'whips', bobbing springs, jointed sticks,
combinations of string and metal foil, in fact anything that will respond to a

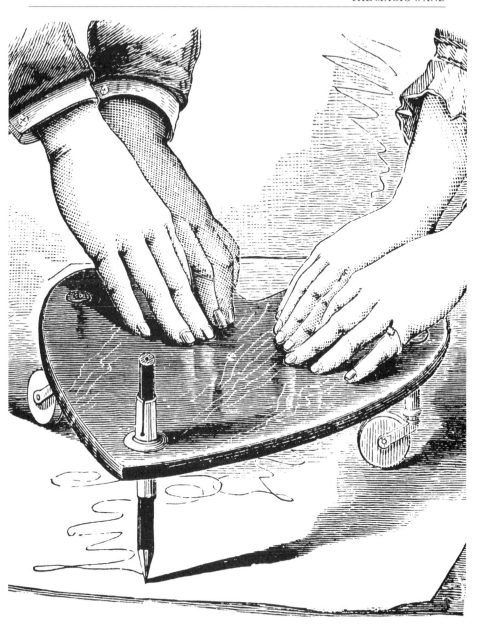

Another example of ideomotor reaction is the movement of this device, known as a planchette, in so-called 'automatic writing'. As with the ouija board, it is said to reveal spirit messages.

slight input of force through a twitch, slope or bounce by the operator, can be used. In many cases the operator will insist on holding against the device a sample of the kind of material that is being sought. The bob of a pendulum is often hollow so that substances – solid or liquid – can be put inside. The French, who dignify the art with the term *radiesthésie* ('sensitivity to radiation'), produce a selection of screw-together pendulums in various colours made of metal, wood and plastic.

The real explanation

The dowser is actually undergoing what is known to psychologists as the 'ideomotor effect'. Unconsciously, he is moving the hand enough to make the larger movement of the device occur, though he will attribute the instrument motion to the divine or supernatural force in which he believes. The same effect causes the motion of the glass on an ouija board, or of the planchette used for 'automatic writing'. In all these events, of course, no information is revealed to the operator except what he already knows.

One episode in the *James Randi: Psychic Investigator* series involved a gentleman who was, I believe, unconsciously using the same technique as the dowsers but regarded his work as an electronic-psychic phenomenon. His name was Norman Knight, and he is principal of the Metaphysical and Psychic Research Society in Berkshire. This organization, according to Mr Knight, has received 'international recognition', though we were not able to verify the claim.

Mr Knight was accompanied by his wife Norma, and a colleague, Ron Turner. They offered to demonstrate a machine which could pick up human thought. It was a small metal box studded with knobs and switches, and with an indicator dial. Mr Knight said it was built for him by a technician, and he admitted that he knew nothing about the design nor the operation of the box, except that it was a detector of his wife's thoughts when she sent them to Mr Turner. He had told our researcher that he knows of no one with more knowledge of healing and the paranormal than himself, but he seems to know nothing at all about his tools.

The little mystery box

Mr Knight has a number of other puzzle boxes of a similar nature that he uses in his strange work, but the box we used on the programme had a pair of wires coming from it, each ending in a metal disc, one steel, the other copper. In preparation for a demonstration, the discs were taped to each of Mr Turner's hands so that his thumb maintained pressure between the disc and the adjoining finger. With the leads in place, Norman then 'tuned' the machine so that it gave out a steady audio tone, and the needle on the indicator dial was steady.

In our experiment, as in others in the series, we preceded the strictly

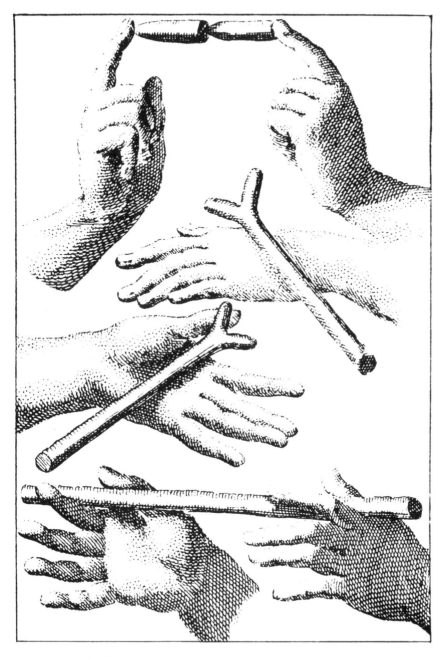

An illustration from a 1793 French book on dowsing, showing various methods of holding devices. All are in poor equilibrium, a necessary feature for the dowsing effect to manifest itself.

controlled test with a demonstration in conditions chosen by the subjects. We called these 'baseline' demonstrations, because they established a standard of performance with which the controlled tests could be compared. This demonstration consisted of Norman giving a hand signal to Mrs Knight, who was seated in the audience facing Ron Turner. She would then think a 'healing thought' toward Mr Turner, whereupon the box would detect this mental image as Mr Turner received it, and the audio signal would rise in frequency.

Earlier in the day, during a dress rehearsal, I was able to handle the wire leads as Mr Knight was tuning the machine. After he had obtained a 'neutral' steady tone, I was easily able to cause the frequency of that tone to rise and fall merely by pressing or relaxing my grip on the metal discs. This machine is basically the same as the one that has been employed by chiropractors and the Scientologists as an 'E-Meter' and by various other practitioners ever since it was developed in Germany in the 1920s. In 1958 a German patent was issued for its circuit as, incredibly enough, a diagnostic tool.

Essentially, it is a carefully balanced electronic circuit which is extremely sensitive to unbalancing by changes in the current passing through it, much as a dowser's rod is sensitive to movement. In the case of Mr Knight's contraption, the box is also 'capacity sensitive', which means that the proximity of any electrically conductive object can also affect the balance. At one point in his rehearsal Norman demonstrated that he could make the audio note change just by touching the wrist of the person who was wired up to the box, but in his estimation this was proof that the device was detecting his presence psychically.

As Norman demonstrated it on the programme, the circuit was merely detecting differences in the electrical resistance of Ron's body between one hand and the other. This resistance amounts to many hundreds of millions of ohms, and will vary greatly with changes in finger pressure on the discs, or in the moistness of the skin, or if the contacts are moved slightly across the hand.

In my personal test during rehearsal, by pressing either of the metal discs against my finger using my thumb, I had improved the area of contact and thus the electrical connection, causing the audio tone of the box to rise. As I had relaxed the pressure, that note had dropped in frequency. If the disc had been taped in place out of reach of my thumb so that I could not improve the connection and thus change the resistance, I could not have produced such an effect.

The definitive test

During the uncontrolled demonstration Ron Turner, seeing the hand signal being given to Mrs Knight by her husband, knew that she was now putting out the appropriate thought signal and, I believe unconsciously, pressed more tightly on the discs, thus producing a rise in the audio tone as I had done. This baseline demonstration was, as expected, successful. Then we conducted our own test, which changed the one parameter that had enabled Ron, however unwittingly, to seem to detect the thought of Mrs Knight. We simply faced him away from Mrs Knight, and I gave the signal for her to send out the healing thought to him. I determined the timing of those signals by consulting my watch and signalling when the second hand reached certain spots on the dial. These spots had been decided upon previously by a randomizing process.

Ron, quite innocently, did not know what to do. The box signalled wildly, even though the only difference in procedure was that he now did not know when he was supposed to be receiving the healing thoughts. The results of our test were so indeterminate that they made no sense at all, except that I could now suggest to these people that they would do well to remove from the experiment the factors that had led me to my unfavourable assessment of the machine. Should they do so, and be able to demonstrate that it works, they would of course immediately receive my $10,000 prize and my full endorsement.

After their poor showing in the test, I asked Norman Knight whether he would permit anyone to look inside the mysterious box. He replied very firmly in the negative, apparently wishing to protect the secret of this marvellous device.

I have included the Knight demonstration in this discussion of dowsing because it is actually the same phenomenon, dressed up in an electronic box.

What do dowsers claim?
Dowsers variously state that they can find water, oil, gold and all other metals and minerals, missing persons, treasure, ruins, bodies, murderers, stolen cars, deadly rays, 'ley lines' (imaginary ancient 'lines of force' in the ground), outlines of old buildings, infected areas on the body, and almost anything the mind can come up with. Some even claim they can find these things not only when actually on the site, but also merely by waving their devices over a map of the area, as we shall see later.

Testing the dowser
Dowsers all over the world have their own organizations dedicated to the art. In the UK the leading such group is the British Society of Dowsers, with headquarters in Ashford, Kent. To obtain the most skilled practitioners to be tested on our programmes, we naturally contacted the BSD and asked their advice.

While waiting for the BSD to respond we went through newspaper

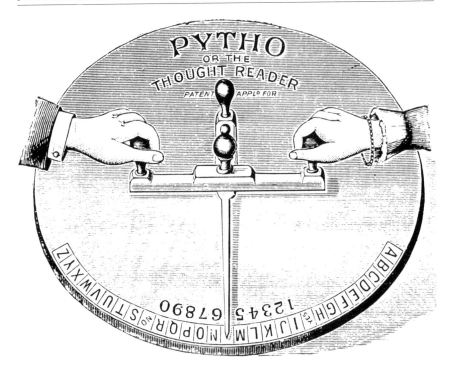

This 1890 device is supposed to be a refinement on the planchette.

articles and previous television programmes that had dealt with individual dowsers, and so found some twenty persons who used a suitable variety of means to perform dowsing feats. At first several of them agreed to appear on our programme. But as the days went by we found that, one by one, our dowsers were dropping out. A number of them claimed, to our amazement, that the BSD had contacted them and 'warned them that Mr James Randi was involved in the presentation' and that they should not have anything to do with the tests! Curious about all this, we telephoned and asked the secretary of the society and the editor of their journal to meet with us and discuss this sudden reluctance to participate or to allow their members to participate in well conducted scientific tests. We said that we would like them to send a representative of the society to the programme to ensure that proper testing procedures were followed, and reminded them that one of the objects of the British Society of Dowsers, as laid down at the founding of the society in 1933, is stated as 'to encourage the study of all matters connected with the perception of radiation by the human organism with or without an instrument'.

To our total confusion, the secretary and editor refused to meet with us, even simply to discuss the problem. It appeared to us that the BSD was not at all willing to have its claims examined, in spite of the stated objects of the organization, for a pamphlet issued by the BSD claims that its purpose is 'to spread information among the members and the public on the use and value of dowsing in all its forms'.

We contacted Sir Charles J. Jessel, president of the BSD, who confirmed that he was not willing for the BSD to be a participant in any presentation that would 'put [dowsing] to the test'. He favoured an approach that would seek to 'find out, in a genuine fashion, about the subject'. This, to my experienced ear, sounds like an uncontrolled demonstration followed by an endless lecture on the wonders of dowsing.

Sir Charles wrote to us that 'the dowsing faculty ... does not always behave to order when real need is not being expressed or fulfilled'. How, then, can he explain the demonstrated fact that in all attempts to find a test object, the dowsers are always 100 per cent successful when they know in advance where the object is, but obtain only chance results when they do not know? Surely there is no 'real need' involved here, yet the 'dowsing faculty' appears to work!

Though the stated purpose of the British Society of Dowsers does not seem to be presently in effect, our programme certainly intended to 'spread information . . . on the use and value of dowsing'. We set out to determine, first, whether there is any actual ability to dowse, after which we were prepared to measure its accuracy.

Sir Charles expressed 'full support' of the warning from the BSD but, flying in the face of that solemn admonition, six brave dowsers agreed to appear, two to comment and four to allow their powers actually to be examined. In retrospect, and in view of Sir Charles's fears, in the introduction to our programme we should have asked all members of the British Society of Dowsers to turn away from the television screen and stop up their ears as we began those tests, lest they suffer the wrath of the society, annoyed that we sought to 'put [dowsing] to the test'.

Ready, set, dowse!

One very complex test that we designed was of a peculiar skill claimed by a few dowsers, called 'map dowsing'. The procedure is so bizarre that we were concerned that it might make a bit of a circus of the show. However, a gentleman named Michael Cook insisted that he could perform it, so we took him on. Map dowsing consists of swinging a pendulum over any piece of paper that represents an area of land, and finding anything from lost children to buried treasure by that means. The map, most claim, can have all co-ordinates removed, can be of any unspecified scale, in colour or not, of an unknown part of the globe, and so on. It is really impossible to suggest any way in which it could work at all. We prepared for Mr Cook a map of an area in Scotland 8 by 12 miles (13 by 19 km). Since he told us he could find a monument such as an ancient abbey, we carefully cropped it so that the area contained only one such monument. We removed everything but roads, co-ordinates, contour lines and regular map symbols, and divided the map into twenty-four squares. The challenge for Mr Cook was to determine with his pendulum the square in which the abbey was located.

A lapse in security

On the afternoon of the show, I was shocked to see one of our team standing outside the TV studio with the enlarged map, 6 feet (1.8 m) long and with a red and white removable indicator affixed which clearly showed the location of the abbey! I knew that Mr Cook was already in the building with his companion, and I was very apprehensive that anyone taking just a quick glance at the map, even from some distance away, could immediately know the solution to the puzzle.

More was to come. Shortly after this, over my objections, there was a camera rehearsal of what would be said if the challenge was successfully met. A word of explanation is appropriate here. All scripts that we prepared for *James Randi: Psychic Investigator* had provided for as many alternate conclusions as we might need. We never presumed that any one of the claimants would lose the challenge – though, from past experience, we expected that they would. A 'win' and a 'loss' were allowed for in every script. It was the 'win' provision for Mr Cook's participation that was being rehearsed, and which called for the correct map square to be displayed in the studio and on the studio and control room TV monitors.

As I stood in the studio and saw the winning solution being shown so obviously, I hoped that no one from Mr Cook's camp was able to take a glance at any of the many available screens. In any case I was committed to proceeding with the rehearsal and the performance as originally planned. We were only one hour away from taping. I want to make one thing perfectly clear: neither I nor any member of the production team imply in any way that Mr Cook or any of his group obtained the information that was carelessly made so easily available. The 'sour grapes' attitude, easily and often assumed by the participants in our programmes when they failed the tests, is not a luxury available to us: we simply will not take that route. As far as I am concerned, Mr Cook's performance on our programme was the result either of his skill as a map dowser, or a remarkable one-in-twenty-four coincidence.

In any case, Michael Cook, after some fussing about over the map with a 'crystal' (actually glass) pendulum on a silver chain, announced that square A2 and another one contained abbeys, but that A2 was the one in which the sought-after abbey was located. He indicated a spot just one mile from the actual location! The other square had no ruins of any kind in it. Could his pendulum truly have determined from a stripped-down map, with that accuracy, where the monument was located? We were reluctant to admit that, but of course we accepted the result.

Following the taping, Michael Cook expressed interest in taking me up on my $10,000 challenge. If we can arrange an experiment that satisfies us both, we'll just do that.

Earlier opinions

Dr Charles Mackay, author of the remarkable book *Extraordinary Popular Delusions*, published in 1841, lists fifty-two species of divination claimed by practitioners. There seems no end of variety to the methods by which people believe they can determine facts by magic.

I have always insisted that claimants for my $10,000 prize must produce proof here and now, not depending upon past performances. The evidence I will now quote from the past is presented, not to disprove dowsing, but to show that claims made by the dowsers that their art has not been shown to be faulted are themselves faulted. In March 1913 extensive tests were carried out in France, which were 'unfavourable to the pretensions of the diviners'. Both these tests and a more comprehensive set carried out at Guildford were reported on by Sir Ray Lankester. Over several months the journal *Sanitary Record*, concerned with water supplies and purification technology, reported on its carefully controlled tests of seven dowsers at Guildford. At a luncheon before the tests, several of the dowsers had declared that such an opportunity was just what they'd been waiting for. On 2 May 1913 the results were published.

> We are able to state here now that several of the [Committee] members were predisposed towards the claims put forward by diviners, and anticipated that the latter would in some degree confirm them. In this, however, they acknowledge they have been disappointed. The diviners have failed to carry conviction. Moreover, as will be seen from the Report, the practically entire absence of agreement of the findings of the diviners who went over the same ground separately; their inability to discover the presence of a large body of water on Site No. 2, which constituted an underground service reservoir; their failure to discover sewers, and a well known spring yielding 50,000 gallons [227,000 litres] per hour, have led the Committee to report adversely against their claims to be able to find hidden or underground waters.

In the issue of *Nature* for 26 March 1927 W.J. Sollas, former president of the Geological Society and a professor of geology at University College, London, reported that

Distinguished geologists have not neglected to subject the powers of the diviner to experimental tests, but always with unfavourable result. ... The question has been investigated by the officers of the U.S. Geological Survey, who found that the successes of the dowsers were less numerous than the laws of chance would have led us to expect ... but they have no time to spare for the exposure of what they have come to regard as a popular delusion.

As for map dowsing, which is a much less frequent subject of claims, a review of a book on the subject in *Nature* in 1940 said,

The fact that such a thing [dowsing over maps with a pendulum] is seriously mentioned [in the book] is calculated to undermine the reader's faith in the author's critical faculty.

Dr Julian Huxley, FRS, said in 1942 that he had been present at a test of this claim at Oxford, and that the diviner failed both with water and with minerals. He added that, in his opinion, the alleged finding of water by means of dowsing over a map was a belief that 'belongs in the Middle Ages' and was 'certainly not worthy of credence'.

Our doubts about dowsing are not at all new, having been expressed as far back as the subject has been known. Voices of reason have been raised in opposition to bizarre ideas of all kinds, even before the scientific method was devised and put into operation.

In search of 'hot spots'

Dowser Michael Cook supported the idea, currently popular in Germany, that there are 'good' and 'bad' locations underfoot everywhere on Earth, and that they can dramatically affect biological functions. 'Geopathic stress' is one name by which the idea is known. We put Mr Cook's idea to a test which he himself suggested. We contacted a husband-and-wife team, Barry and Sue Wood, who are 'hot spot' dowsers. The Woods visited our studio before the taping of this programme and picked out what they designated as a good, a bad and a neutral spot. These were marked on the studio floor.

For clarity, let us refer to these three spots as A, B and C. According to the Woods, this was the ranking:

A neutral
B good
C bad

Michael Cook was asked to give his opinion on these three locations, which we had clearly marked on the floor with large blue circles. Swinging his pendulum over spot A, he said he found it was '30 per cent bad'. In my

BAD   GOOD

innocence I assumed that this meant it to be 70 per cent good. Spot B, Cook said, was '45 per cent good,' which I figured was equivalent to 55 per cent bad, while the '70 per cent bad' evaluation Cook gave to spot C was therefore 30 per cent good. I should have known better than to assume that he used such a straightforward scoring system, and it was some time before we found out exactly what he meant.

In fact his judgement was:

A bad (30 per cent) – 'detrimental to health'
B good (45 per cent) – 'good for health'
C bad (70 per cent) – 'detrimental to health'

He did not rate any of the spots as neutral.

At that point we introduced Mike Aherne, the British bodybuilding champion, who was to test all three spots to see if his strength declined, increased or remained the same on any of them. Mike was asked to first show us how he could depress a 'Bullworker' spring-loaded exercise device while standing away from any of the three selected spots. This was a 'baseline' determination, since performing this feat at arm's length, as he did it, was obviously a real test of his ability; perspiration stood out on his brow. Next, he went to spots A, B and C in rapid succession and repeated the feat. Mike's report on his performance was:

A a bit harder than the baseline
B a bit more difficult than A
C a bit more difficult than B

That Mike's strength declined somewhat as he went through three repetitions was no great surprise to us. It was what we might have expected.

A confusion of terms and values

It's difficult to establish clearly what the results of these demonstrations meant. Everyone had agreed on spot C being a relatively 'bad' spot, but both Mike Aherne and Michael Cook disagreed with the Woods about spot A being 'neutral' and Mike Aherne had found B – the spot all dowsers had designated as 'good' – to be 'worse' than spot A, and spot A to be the 'best' of all, rather than 'neutral' or 'bad', as it had been designated by the dowsers.

The only thing that was clear was that not much of a case was made for the 'geopathic stress' idea, nor for agreement between the dowsers. But it had been almost inevitable that the results would be inconclusive, because there was no way we could think of to compare the three methods of evaluation objectively.

Cancer from E-rays?

Dr Keith Mumby, one of our guests, was once a practising GP, and is now a clinical ecologist. Basing his beliefs on an early book from Germany, Dr Mumby endorses the idea of *Erde-Strahlen* or 'Earth rays'. These are supposed to be mysterious radiations that are emitted from unknown sources deep in the ground, giving rise to 'hot spots.' These spots, say the believers, cannot be detected by instruments of any kind, but are believed to exist because dowsers – and only dowsers – can sense them. In Germany these invisible rays and 'hot spots' are accepted by almost everyone – even government agencies, which pay dowsers to relocate desks of workers away from the positions where E-rays can pass through them; hospital beds are similarly moved about to protect patients from cancer.

Keith Mumby told us he had discovered that a certain street in York, which we do not name for obvious reasons, was obviously full of E-rays because 'four or five' persons had died there recently from cancer. He told us also that dowsers would be able to detect those rays. We took two independent dowsers to three streets, one of which was the deadly one; but this was not identified to the dowsers, and they declared that it was free of 'hot spots', in spite of the dreadful diagnosis made by Dr Mumby.

To show that even amateurs without medical degrees can determine simple facts, our researchers called the Yorkshire Cancer Registry and asked for information about reported cancer deaths in that street. Their spokesperson, Professor Joslin, told us that in the last five years only three persons had died there. That figure, said Professor Joslin, was not at all unusual. 'I find this figure average . . . and certainly not something to be concerned about,' he said. 'This is the sort of figure I would expect to see from an average residential street.' Especially if elderly persons were resident there, even a slightly higher figure would be normal.

Why was Dr Keith Mumby not able to research the data about that street before declaring that 'hot spots' – which even the dowsers could not detect – were responsible for the non-existent high cancer death rate? It is unfortunately often the case that believers in foolish ideas accept anything that seems to validate those ideas, without troubling to check it.

Finding minerals with a stick

The closing performer in our dowsing programme was an amiable gentleman named Clive Thompson. He brought with him, at our request, the substance that he felt most able to detect reliably with his dowsing rod. This turned out to be zinc ore, and before the taping he demonstrated to his own and others' satisfaction that his stick reacted strongly to the presence of the ore, though he did not choose to try this preliminary test in a randomized double-blind manner, as we were about to do.

Before the cameras for the proper test, Clive was to try to find under which of seven cardboard boxes we had located a piece of his ore. He had discovered, so he told us, that for some reason his powers showed themselves best when the boxes were coloured green; other colours inhibited his dowsing stick. So we had eight identical green boxes prepared.

First we asked him to establish a baseline by showing us that his dowsing stick performed properly when he knew that the sample was in place. On a separate small podium, we showed him that a piece of ore was placed beneath one of the green boxes. He in turn showed us, twice, that his stick moved properly to indicate the presence of the zinc ore under the box. Then, abandoning that sample, that box and that podium, because he had said that 'residual vibrations' of the ore would stay behind to confound his powers, we turned to the test area.

Seven podiums were in place, well separated from one another. There was a green box on top of each one. Backstage, a few moments before, I had selected at random one folded paper from a group of seven, each bearing a digit from one to seven. I had not looked at it, but placed it in my pocket. This was to be the number of the box under which the stage hand would place the ore sample. He would know, from examining the six remaining papers, under which box it should be placed. This now constituted a double-blind test, with controls as perfect as we could achieve.

We knew that if chance was acting rather than dowsing ability, Clive Thompson would probably take three or four guesses to locate the ore. However, since he had just shown us that his baseline was 100 per cent accurate, he should have located it on the very first trial.

On the third trial, he was right.

After the taping Mr Thompson objected that the studio conditions had been 'artificial', but I reminded him that his baseline demonstrations had shown that he had failed only when he did not know the location of the zinc ore. And, in an informal demonstration in the hallway outside the studio before the taping, Mr Thompson had shown definitively that his dowsing stick worked when he knew where the ore was. True to the dowsers' tradition, Clive would have none of my explanation.

Do dowsers detect E-rays?
Dowsing fans objected strongly that *James Randi: Psychic Investigator* had failed to test the most basic of their claims: that they could detect flowing

water. I must point out that not only was such a plan beyond our budget, but despite several weeks of advertising and telephone calls, we could find no dowser who would agree to perform such a test for us. The British Society of Dowsers, who certainly could have supplied appropriate persons, had refused to do so.

I had also just returned from an extensive investigation of the water-dowsing claim in Germany, where tests had established once again that the assertions of dowsers do not match their actual performances. I had acted as advisor for the Gesellschaft zur wissenschaftlichen Unter-suchungen von Parawissenschaften (GWUP for short, meaning 'Society for the Scientific Investigation of Para-Science'), a German sceptics' group which was determined to test this specific claim of the dowsers, especially since the government had just spent some DM400,000 on a rather naive set of tests with highly overvalued results in their efforts to solve the mystery of *Erde-Strahlen* or E-rays. Professors König and Betz, the authors of a book on the government tests, had been invited to attend, but declined to do so, as well as refusing to give the GWUP the names of any dowsers they had tested, or even to put the dowsers in touch with the GWUP secretary. Their reasons for this lack of co-operation were not made clear.

Apparently the German scientists had never heard of the disastrous affair of the 'N-rays' that so embarrassed the French back in 1903, when René Blondlot, a physicist of Nancy, announced his discovery of strange radiations that were soon confirmed by dozens of scientists, until a single physicist sent by *Nature* magazine showed them that not only were their experimental processes faulty, but their rays were totally imaginary. The physicist, Dr Robert Wood, had surreptitiously removed an aluminium prism from Blondlot's apparatus, and stood back while the lab workers – including Blondlot himself – continued to detect and measure rays that could not possibly be there, since the prism was the heart of the device. The N-rays affair provides the best single example of scientific error through experimenters' bias and expectation, an example which might yet be exceeded by the present German fascination with the equally imaginary E-rays.

The GWUP dowsing tests
At Kassel, north of Frankfurt, the GWUP set up a very efficient site in co-operation with a local television station. It consisted of a pipe of suitable size buried 20 inches (50 cm) beneath a level section of field, through which a very large flow of water could be directed from a switching valve. The test area was protected by a large tent, and the position of the buried pipe was prominently marked by a broad red and white stripe. The challenge for the dowsers was not to find the pipe, but only to say whether water was flowing in it or not.

In response to advertisements, we obtained thirty eager dowsers, mostly from Germany but also from Denmark, Austria and France. To assure them that all was being done in a carefully controlled manner, and that they had an assurance of fair and proper treatment during the tests, we demonstrated to them that all stages of the procedure were to be covered by constant video surveillance from all angles, using time-coded and synchronized tapes.

Each dowser would be required to perform ten 'open' trials in which he would know whether or not the water was flowing, and he would have to show that he obtained 100 per cent results at that time. This set of trials would provide us with a baseline from which to judge the subsequent twenty 'closed' trials which immediately followed, in which he would not know whether the water was flowing. In all cases, both with the 'open' and 'closed' tests, turning the valve on or off was decided by the selection of a marked ball from a bag.

Also available for each dowser to try was an auxiliary test using a set of ten opaque boxes, one of which contained any object or substance they cared to select. We had gold, silver, iron, copper and a powerful magnet available, and the subjects were free to bring anything else they wished to use. Again, baseline tests were performed, then ten actual test trials.

First things first

Wisely, in retrospect, we asked each dowser to make a statement in advance of the trials expressing any objections he might have to the way we proposed to conduct them. We then adjusted the procedure to meet every objection. Next, each subject was asked to use his dowsing instrument to scan the area in which the test was to be performed, to see if any underground distractions were present. This was done because dowsers frequently complain, when tests prove negative, that some subterranean river, buried treasure, deadly rays, lodestone or other diversion disturbed their performance. The results of that preliminary scan, as you will see shortly, proved very interesting. But whether the anomalies were imaginary or not, in each case we were able to arrange the procedure so that the dowsers could avoid any effect they might expect.

At the end of three days of testing, we announced the results of almost a thousand items of data to the assembled dowsers. An examination of their results had revealed exactly what would be expected according to chance. Immediately several of them offered strenuous objections, one even claiming that we had buried extra pipes underground to distract their dowsing powers. Another man, who was so incredibly pompous that he refused to sit with the rest of them, mumbled about lawsuits and other dreadful methods of revenge, but finally packed up his assortment of bobbing springs, swinging rods and pendulums and drove off in a spray of gravel and dust.

Do they *want* to know?

While I must salute the dowsers of Germany as well as those dowsers who volunteered to participate in our tests at Granada for their willing involvement in our search for proof, I have to wonder whether the dowsing community in general really wants to know whether its members can do what they claim. Certainly, the attitude of the British Society of Dowsers indicates that they are fearful of examination, and the society has set up many an obstacle to proper inquiry. It is my intention to confer with responsible advocates of this claim, with the intent of organizing a once-and-for-all massive test of dowsing. Whether that goal will ever be realized depends entirely upon the goodwill, sincerity and dedication of the dowsers themselves.

No consistency of performance

You will recall that in these tests we had asked all the dowsers to scan the test area in advance for any anomalies that might distract their powers. They did this one at a time, and as soon as each had finished, he or she was segregated from the others, so that no information could be exchanged. The result was that each performer made an independent assessment of the site without conferring with the others.

Now, one of the questions that must be answered about this art is whether two dowsers can find the same things in the same area. In the past it has been shown that they cannot, and our tests showed the same result. None of our thirty dowsers found the same anomalies, though all but one found some anomaly. A few thought they'd found raging underground rivers, some said they had detected buried rock or metal masses, while others indicated deadly E-rays issuing from the site at specific points – but never the same points. Then when all thirty determinations were overlaid on the plan of the 49 by 49 foot (15 by 15 m) test site, it was literally covered with every sort of line, point, area, patch and intersection that could be imagined. Obviously, only one of the dowsers could have been right, and possibly all were wrong.

Why do governments spend money on it?

One dowser in our audience waved a book about while demanding to know why, in my opinion, the German government had spent such a large sum on a dowsing investigation, as if that somehow proved that there must therefore be a genuine dowsing phenomenon. I'd like to point out that back in the beginning of the Nazi era in Germany, a considerable amount was spent in training selected SS warriors to perfect their dowsing skills so that they could locate fabulous buried treasures to finance the new political party and the coming war. That money was not well spent, at least from the Nazis' point of view. Recently the Norwegian government backed the Red Cross in an investigation of dowsing as a means of locating buried avalanche victims. Its failure ended the official interest in the technique and any willingness to invest more kroner in the idea.

The expenditure of money by bureaucrats on such projects might only indicate their naivety. I predict that any amount of continued expenditure for this purpose will result, as it always has, in disappointment.

Dowsing for the police?

The dowsers, bless 'em, have a sense of hyperbole that is unsurpassed. They blithely claim all manner of successes, because they are seldom asked for proof of their fantasies. One variety that we seldom see is the 'police dowser'. But such people do exist.

One of the most notorious serial killer mysteries in the USA became known as the 'Hillside Strangler' case. Over several years a number of women had been murdered in southern California, and later in Washington state, in a way which left police baffled. California dowser Verne McGuire breathlessly told a writer for the *Ridgecrest Daily Independent* newspaper how he had helped to solve that case. McGuire told the *Independent* that the police refused to listen to him at first, but that finally he and his dowser friends

> got the Los Angeles police and sheriff's department, the Marshall Service and the Federal Bureau of Investigation. They told us that if we knew where the Hillside Strangler was, we must be involved with him. To prove we weren't involved, we had to find him in such a way that it was impossible we could be involved, so we moved in with some cops. Then he killed again. Because he would now be on the run, we thought this was the best time to look for him.

And how did this intrepid band of amateurs propose to find the Strangler? By waving their pendulums over a map of the area. According to McGuire, they actually located him by this means, and sent the police to a certain spot on the map where he was found in his car sitting in a service station. In the boot of the car were articles of clothing and a purse belonging to one of his victims. When the murderer was arrested, said McGuire, 'He knew they had him. We were vindicated.'

A simple inquiry, and the truth

Really? Not according to the police, who in fact solved the case by totally different means. First of all, the Hillside Strangler turned out to be two persons working together, not just one. The US Marshall's Office was not involved in the investigation at all, nor was the FBI. Both those organizations denied that they'd ever even heard of McGuire and his dowsing chums, and the places that McGuire had identified as their offices in his account have never served as such. As for the Los Angeles police, who solved the case, they reported that

> McGuire's statements concerning the 'Hillside Strangler' case and his involvement are in conflict with what occurred. One of the suspects was arrested in Bellingham, Washington, and the second was arrested at his place of business in the city of Glendale. No clothing belonging to any of the victims was ever found.

Bellingham is a very long way from where McGuire said he discovered the murderer; in fact it was not even on the map he dowsed over.

Electrical engineer David J. Simmons, a reader of the *Ridgecrest Daily Independent*, was enraged at the statement made by McGuire in that newspaper. Simmons made a few simple telephone calls that discovered the misrepresentation, and submitted his findings to the editor of the newspaper. What happened? Nothing. The newspaper already had its wide-eyed story, and the editor apparently thought that his readers did not deserve the truth.

The original story told by McGuire has made the rounds on the gee-whiz circuit, and I had it thrown up to me some months before at a lecture I gave in Florida. Not having Simmons's research data at that time – since it had never been published – I was forced to admit that I simply didn't know any of the facts about the case. Another win for the media who pander to a credulous public.

Living or dead

A medium who originated in Hungary but has been active in the UK for many years, Agnes Freeman, told us that she could determine, by swinging a pendulum over a photograph, whether the person shown was dead or alive. She claimed this ability was very positive, and always worked with '99¾ per cent' accuracy. We invited her to appear on our programme.

We presented her with five photographs early in the afternoon before our studio meeting. We also had gigantic versions of the same photos prepared, and Agnes went from one to the other. She decided that the first four were alive, and the last one was deceased. Chance alone, for example by tossing a coin, would give Agnes either two or three correct guesses (on average 2½). She got just three correct. Unfortunately she also gave us readings on the persons involved, which were far from correct, and the person she nominated as 'dead' was the father of one of our researchers and very much alive.

PURVEYORS OF SPIRITS

The great survival question, with
an excursion into fairyland.

CHAPTER 4

PURVEYORS OF SPIRITS

How can we know the state of the dead,
seeing we hardly know the state of the living?
Confucius, 550-477 BC

Probably no question has preoccupied the human race more than whether we possess a soul which survives bodily death. We believe that other species are not aware of their own mortality, though that seems difficult to establish with any certainty.

Over the years famous figures such as David Hume, Sir William Crookes, Sir Arthur Eddington, Thomas Edison, Harry Houdini and Sir Oliver Lodge occupied themselves with this eternal question. But one figure in recent history stands out as the most important and influential advocate of the reality of life after death. Sir Arthur Conan Doyle, creator of Sherlock Holmes but also an ardent promoter of the spiritualistic cause, spent much time at spiritualist seances where the most improbable events were staged. He happily accepted fantastic claims that most of us would find very difficult to believe, or even to listen to without amusement.

The Cottingley fairies

As an example of Sir Arthur's naivety, we can look at a strange tale which concerns a different kind of spirit. It is remarkable how this otherwise level-headed man chose to endorse a story told by two little Yorkshire girls in Bradford simply because it fitted in with his beliefs.

Elsie and Frances told everyone that they had seen fairies in a place called Cottingley Glen, and in 1917 they said that they had even taken photographs of the sprites as proof of their stories. Conan Doyle, before he even saw the photographs – and he never did meet the girls – swallowed the whole tale and set about promoting the existence of fairies, elves and other wee creatures which he now firmly believed were flitting about in the woods.

Conan Doyle even took lantern slides of the Cottingley photos to America with him on a lecture tour. The rights to the photos themselves were given by the girls' mother to the Theosophy movement, which embraced belief in wood sprites and such beings. Years later, when Elsie saw a photograph of a huge church the Theosophists had built with the proceeds of sales of the photos, she grumbled that she and Frances hadn't seen a penny for their labours, while millions had been raised from their work.

Sir Arthur was a bit of a snob, which was one reason for his credulity. Victorian society, of which he was a leading product, rigidly catalogued people according to class. He reasoned, therefore, that two adolescent females 'from the artisan class' could not possibly deceive an aristocrat such as himself. And that, for him, settled the matter. Such a man was not accustomed to being told he was wrong.

Only a few years ago the two who had perpetrated this rather delicious hoax on Conan Doyle − and, through him, on the whole world − died. They had never been willing to admit openly that their photos were fakes, but along the way they dropped tantalizing hints. The elder, Elsie, even owned up to part of the hoax on a BBC *Nationwide* programme. I exchanged correspondence with her from 1978, and she admitted to me that their 'little joke fell flat on its face right away', and explained that, had it not been for Conan Doyle seizing the opportunity to discover and champion yet another supernatural discovery, their photographs would have just remained 'out of sight in a drawer' where her father had thrown them.

The incredible acceptance

Elsie was amazed that people accepted their hoax. She told me, 'Surely you know that there can not be more than one grown-up person in every five million who would take our fairies seriously.' Elsie's dad was dismayed. He asked his wife, 'How could a brilliant man like Conan Doyle believe such a thing?'

But Elsie was quite disturbed by me, as well. She began one of her letters to me with 'Dear Mid Summer Night's Dream banisher Mr Randi', but then she closed it by inviting me to visit her, admonishing, 'But for heavens sake, if you come, no Fairy talk, please!'

The photos were prepared by using paper cutouts of fairies drawn by Elsie from originals in a popular children's book, *Princess Mary's Gift Book*. It was that simple. Yet the sisters created a hugely successful monster that lives on even today − despite the proof of trickery − in the pages of sensational journals and in books that pander to the silly.

The great puzzle is why the Cottingley fairy photographs were ever accepted in the first place. They are very obviously fakes, as can be easily proven. The first, and the most famous, of the five photographs shows Frances with four tiny fairies in full flight. What is often ignored is the image of a small waterfall in the background behind Frances, which Mr Brian Coe, curator of the Kodak Museum in Harrow, assured me could only have been registered on the slow film of that era by a lengthy time exposure. How is it, then, that the fairies themselves, with their fluttering butterfly

The illustration in *Princess Mary's Gift Book* from which Elsie prepared the paper cutouts of the fairies.

wings, are so sharp and clear? That rapid motion would have required a shutter speed that was far beyond the capabilities of the camera that was used to take that picture, particularly in view of the subdued light on the scene, which would have required a modern fast film if the picture were not to be impossibly underexposed. The four other photos display similar anomalies.

The truth emerges

Now, one might have expected that the Society for Psychical Research – already well organized when these marvellous pictures were first publicized – would have taken a strong interest in them and in what seemed, to some, to have been an authenticated sighting. Perhaps the society already believed in fairies and didn't need any proof of their existence, nor further investigation of such an established phenomenon. In any case it was a quarter-century before the SPR examined the evidence. In 1945 – to the society's credit – the members decided that they were now 'sceptical of the reality of fairies in general and of the Cottingley Fairies in particular'.

My 1980 book *Flim-Flam!* pointed out extensive and substantial evidence against the reality of the Cottingley fairies. The *British Journal of Photography* understandably took until 1975 even to mention these photos, and then in 1982 ran a series of quite devastating articles by editor Geoffrey

'Frances and the Fairies', the first and most important of the Cottingley photographs.

Crawley that should have effectively ended the controversy with a bang. Despite such thorough research, however, no amount of evidence will serve to dissuade believers; they are determined to remain deceived.

Conan Doyle's easy acceptance of such matters indicates that we can question his declared faith in spirit mediums, which at the time was instrumental in bringing legitimacy to their claims.

A session with Maureen Flynn

In Conan Doyle's time mediums conducted seances in dark rooms. Nowadays these affairs usually take place in more cheerful surroundings. Maureen Flynn, known as one of Britain's most successful mediums, conducts classes in which she claims to develop her students' mediumistic talents.

We saw something of those methods when we featured Ms Flynn on our programme. The results raised questions about just how successful these students are. We recorded their opinions of her, which could hardly have been more favourable, or more vague. One described something as being both hard and soft at the same time, there were obscure references to

An advertisement for night lights was said – wrongly – to be the source of the Cottingley fairy pictures.

allegorical qualities, and much fitting of theories to facts seemed to be going on. But our programme was dedicated to actually testing Maureen's mediumistic claims. We began by watching an uncontrolled 'audience reading', a demonstration in which she relayed 'spirit messages' to our studio audience.

As we expected, many common personal names were thrown out for acceptance. Following Maureen's audience reading, I asked them how many of them, for example, could accept the name Taylor which she had offered them. The electronic voting machine we used showed an acceptance of 30 per cent. As for the heart and chest condition of a grandfather she had proposed for consideration, it was inescapable that most of those present could accept that; the voting showed a 55 per cent agreement. Such 'hits' are hardly remarkable.

A classic example of the method

The best analysis of a spiritualist's claims can be obtained by examination of a 'one-on-one' reading, in which there are fewer chances of the reader merely striking lucky than when messages are offered to a large studio or theatre audience.

Surprisingly, that ideal situation was offered to us by Maureen herself. She had brought along to our studio a satisfied customer, a gentleman who gave us an audio tape of a 30 minute reading that Ms Flynn had recently done for him. He expressed himself as being very satisfied with the accuracy of that reading. After I had listened to the content of the tape and had it transcribed, I found his opinion astonishing. The reading not only provided typical instances of the methods used in these performances, but also gave us proof that, as conjurors know, spectators are seldom able to recall what actually took place or was said to them, and even when correctly informed later will not be swayed in their firmly held convictions, no matter how hard the evidence.

Before the cameras, I asked the customer if Maureen had thrown out a lot of names for him to accept or reject when she gave the reading. He confidently said that she had offered only six names. And, he added, all six had been 'hits'. Let's look at this well accepted reading to see just how accurate it was, and how well the customer (whom we shall simply call 'R') recalled the data he'd so gladly paid for.

The reading

To begin R's reading, Maureen offered 'Mark' and 'Michael' as significant names. R replied that Michael 'means more than Mark'. She said that she wanted 'to put Michael close' to R. He told her that Michael was his eldest son. They both now dismissed Mark completely. That guess didn't work, so Mark was gone and forgotten!

One of the occult powers claimed by performers is the ability to read with the fingertips. Here, Léonide Pigeaire demonstrates her skill at what is merely a conjuring trick.

Next Maureen said that she'd 'got a lady here' and that the lady said that R had three children. R said no, he had only two. The 'lady' was now forgotten for the moment. To rescue a bad guess, Maureen asked R if he had lost one son. He answered that he had not. Maureen insisted that there was a third child, and now switched to a girl. When that failed, she offered that this non-existent girl, who a moment ago had been tried on as his daughter, was perhaps 'like a part of the family'. This didn't work either, and in a desperate attempt to save the 'girl' guess, Maureen openly asked R, 'Do you have a female dog?' He couldn't accept this, either. This problematical girl promptly vanished somewhere, we presume with Mark, wherever he went.

Maureen now returned to the unrecognized lady who, she said, now 'feels like [R's] mother' and again asked R something: whether his mother was deceased. He said that she was. Now she asked who 'Derek' was. R told her that he had a nephew of that name.

Maureen told R that his mother was supportive of him and was watching over him. He eagerly agreed to this startling revelation. She told R, 'I must be going back something over five years.' He answered, 'Oh, yes' to this, though there was no question asked and it was not said what this 'going back' was supposed to relate to.

Maureen said that R 'had hair' when his mother died. He agreed. She asked him, 'Who's John?' and he didn't respond. Maureen said, 'He feels like a brother.' R didn't affirm anything. She then asked, 'Does Jim make more sense?' R didn't respond to this name, but then he answered, 'John — only in a business sense.'

Next Maureen suggested that 'John is a partner or somebody that you work with' and R replied, 'Sort of' but then said that John was not a partner of his. She told R, 'No', agreeing with what he had just finished telling her, and then she added that R worked with John, which he also had just told her! And R agreed with Maureen.

Maureen went on to ask about an aunt's husband that never existed, trying the names 'Colin' and 'Kevin' on for size and, when they didn't fit, jumping to 'Katherine' and 'Karen', neither of which worked either. Then she tried the name 'May', missed on that one too, attempted to turn it into a birthday in the month of May, asked R to identify whose birthday it was, and when this also didn't work, she changed May into Mary! Happily for her, R said he could accept that name. But when she tried to make Mary his aunt, R told her that she was a cousin by marriage. Maureen asked him if she was dead. R told her she was, though that was hardly needed; he had already said, 'She was a cousin by marriage.'

A plethora of names

Hardly a third of the way into this reading, we can see that this is an endless series of throwing out names, missing most of them, misidentifying the people, changing direction, discarding any attempts that failed, and blatantly asking direct questions of the sitter rather than telling him things, which was supposed to be the purpose of the reading in the first place. Just for the record, in 30 minutes Maureen Flynn threw out these names:

Alan, Alice, Alfred, Ann, Bill, Charlie, Colin, Connie, David, Derek, Eileen, Ellen, Florrie, Frank, Fred, George, Jim, Joe, John, Karen, Katherine, Kevin, Lillian, Lisa, Liz, Lynne, Mark, Mary, May, Michael, Rob, Ron, Shirley, Sid, Sidney, Stanley, Steve.

That's thirty-seven names! Incredibly enough, she also asked her sitter to make associations with any names (male or female, living or dead, family or friend, business acquaintance or anyone else) that began with either N or L, and he could not do so. When he volunteered the name 'Bennett' to her, Maureen declared that she'd found the 'N' she was searching for, because N, she said, is the 'dominant' sound in the name.

A bare nine of these thirty-seven names were 'accepted' by R. Please remember that this satisfied customer recalled that only six names had been tried, and that all six were 'hits'. Also note the rather wide spectrum of acceptability for these quite common names that are being offered to the client: we have a son, a brother, a grandfather and a nephew (who are close enough in the family to be admissible) but then we must also accept an adopted nephew, a fellow worker, a cousin by marriage, a lodger, and the neighbour's dog! Only two of these persons or animals were deceased, and those are the kind of personalities that we are supposed to be contacting through a spirit medium. Finally, R's own mother and aunt, who we are told are supplying all this fuzzy information to Maureen, are among none of the thirty-seven names that were tried.

Hits, misses and guesses

Though a thorough analysis of the reading given for 'R' is difficult, a cursory examination gives three significant statistics.

1 Maureen used the phrase 'I think ...' (or 'I don't think ...') twenty-five times. This is a way of 'trying on' a guess for acceptance. That was done about once every minute of the reading.

2 She asked fifty-nine times for direct, factual information from the sitter. That's about once every 30 seconds.

3 She made 63 guesses, more than two a minute, of which 49 (78 per cent) were wrong.

Can anyone really consider this reading to have been a successful one? Apparently Maureen Flynn and her happy customer are convinced that it meets their standards. When I asked Maureen if this was a typical reading, she agreed that it was. Can it be – and I propose this quite seriously – that Maureen Flynn and her colleagues cannot see that the hunting-and-searching, hot-and-cold rummaging about that they are doing must invariably lead to some sort of link between the great number of probes they are throwing out, and the facts of the sitter's life? The likelihood of success is, of course, greatly increased by allowing past, present and future events and relationships to be included, and such wide ranging of the imagination is not only expected by the mediums, but is encouraged. More importantly, it should be evident that any association thus obtained may not then be attributed to the presence – or even the existence – of supernatural forces or entities. It is not 'evidence' of any sort, but the inevitable result of a willing if largely unconscious collusion between the medium and the sitter.

The Davenports – spiritualists?

The American Davenport brothers, Ira and William, caused a major sensation in the late nineteenth century with a spectacular and puzzling vaudeville stage act which seemed to support belief in spiritualist doctrine. It consisted of being tied hand and foot and then being locked into a large cabinet with an assortment of props, after which bells would sound, musical instruments would be played, strange hands would appear through openings in the cabinet, and a bewildered victim taken from the audience would have his clothes turned inside out and various other indignities would be inflicted on him. The cabinet was often opened quickly right in the midst of these events, and the two Davenports were always found to be still securely bound and seemingly 'in trance'.

Many who saw this act attributed the effects to spirit forces; it seemed impossible for the Davenports – and others who imitated their act – to have done the tricks by other than supernatural means. But we must remember that modern stage magicians – such as Mr Paul Daniels – regularly perform equally confounding feats, and we do not ascribe to them any diabolical powers or collusion. Today, Glen Falkenstein and his wife Frances (who is the daughter of Willard the Wizard, who made the act famous) perform an incredible replication of the Davenport act which might even be better than the original.

Ira Davenport wrote in 1909 to the famous American magician and escape artist, Harry Houdini, giving an explanation of their philosophy concerning the act that he and his brother had performed.

We never in public affirmed our belief in spiritualism, that we regarded as no business of the public, nor did we offer our entertainments as the results of sleight of hand, nor on the other hand as spiritualism, we let our friends and foes settle that as best they could between themselves.

The escape act that Houdini himself developed was inspired by a Davenport-type act he saw in 1887, when he was just thirteen years old. The budding magician who was to revolutionize the art of conjuring realized that the performers were freeing themselves in order to carry out their clever deceptions, and he decided to make it clear to his own audience that what he did was accomplished solely by dexterity and skill. This he never failed to do.

On our TV programme I established to the audience's satisfaction that such feats are quite possible without selling one's soul or removing one's skeleton. The fact that the audience did not know the *modus operandi* of the tricks certainly did not require them to invoke a supernatural explanation.

Ghost photography

Spiritualists have long embraced a phenomenon that they believe to prove their basic premiss of survival after death. They call it 'spirit photography'. If I were to ask a person of average intelligence what the first photo here shows, I expect I'd receive an opinion that someone has placed a piece of Swiss cheese on this lady's head, that she has a runny nose, or that some cotton wool has been teased out and stuck on her chin. But to the spiritualists, this is 'ectoplasm' or an 'ethereal body' in the process of forming.

The second photograph would appear to show us a lady who has perhaps had recourse to the cooking sherry, nodding off before a paper cutout with a length of white cloth fastened to it, stuck up on the wall with a drawing pin above her head. Not so, say the believers; this is a 'spiritoid form draped in a white ectoplasmic veil'.

Sir Arthur Conan Doyle was, as might be expected, a popular target for the spirit photographers to summon up after his death in 1930. In a book which describes the process of spirit photography, an example of Sir Arthur's appearance to the spirit camera is shown. Below the supposed spirit photo is an ordinary one of the author in his prime, a photo that was and still is widely published and easily available. I prepared a transparent copy of it, and when I turned it over left to right it fitted precisely over the spirit photo, agreeing in detail, lighting and expression. It seems obvious that the spirit photo is merely a cutout of a reversed photo placed in what appears to be cotton wool. If this is not so, it is a remarkable coincidence that these two photos, taken so many years apart, are identical except for the reversal.

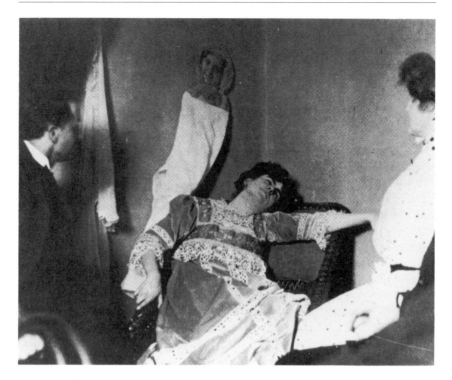

An example of so-called 'spirit photography' that is celebrated in the history of the art.

This is another photograph that is widely admired among spiritualists as evidence that the dead return.

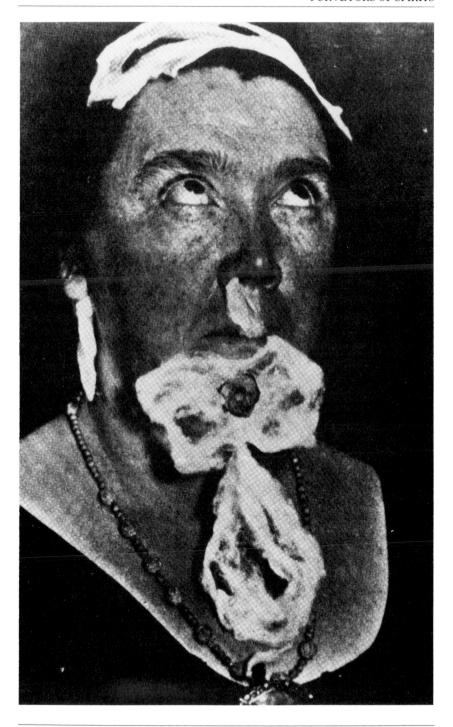

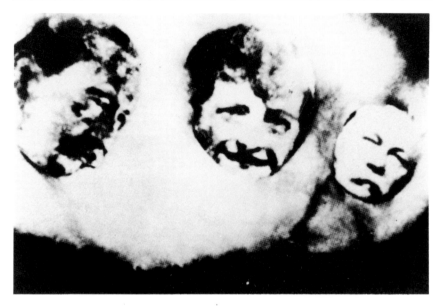

A supposed spirit photograph of Conan Doyle, with the real photo it was apparently copied from.

Now as then

Lest you should think that such giddy ideas ceased when the Victorian and Edwardian ages passed into history, I must tell you that only a few years ago a man in the USA named Ted Serios was said to have the ability to project his thoughts on to the film inside a Polaroid camera. The method involved a simple optical device, yet the trick managed to fool a Freudian psychiatrist, several parapsychologists and a number of other learned individuals, in spite of definitive exposure of the trick. Again, the believers are determined to remain deceived.

The Serios trick has become part of my repertoire when I deliver my lectures.

A DIVINE TOUCH

Take up thy bed. And fall down.

CHAPTER 5

A DIVINE TOUCH

An ignorant doctor is the aide-de-camp of death.
Avicenna, AD 980-1037

In 1989 my book *The Faith Healers* was published. The task of preparing that book was one of the most difficult things I have ever had to do, since it involved interviewing people whom I knew to be dying of various ailments, many of them because they had put themselves in the hands of religious healers. In all, I pursued a hundred and four individuals who either claimed they had been healed, or for whom healers or relatives had claimed healing. Just half of them were already dead before I got around to interviewing them, and a few of the remainder were in such poor condition that they could not see me.

Thirty of the remaining fifty-two merely imagined they were suffering from the ailments, and medical examination had found no trace of them. In one case a woman exulted to me that she'd been cured of throat cancer, and happily produced a letter from her doctor stating that she had no indications of that disease. When I called the doctor, in exchange for my agreement that neither he nor the patient would be identified by name he told me that this woman's mother had died of throat cancer years before, and every time the woman had a sore throat she claimed that what she believed to be a hereditary disease had now afflicted her. She had obtained the letter from him ostensibly to use in getting a job, but it had been used to establish her 'cure' at the hands of a local faith healer. The doctor despondently pointed out that the woman was a heavy smoker and so had an excellent chance of really getting throat cancer.

During the preparation of my manuscript for the book, my repeated requests to the healers themselves for documentation of their successes went unanswered. In spite of their claims that they'd healed thousands of people, not a single one of them produced the identities of those persons, nor any documentation. 'God doesn't need to be examined or challenged' was the answer I often heard.

An imaginary miracle

A typical case was that of one person who, because he had an unusual name, was quite easy to find after I saw him mentioned in a faith-healer's glossy newsletter. There it was asserted that this man had been healed of diabetes and that he had 'held' his healing for three years. (The healers say, when the disease doesn't go away, that the subject has lost faith and thus failed to 'hold' his blessing. In this way, neither God nor the healer can be blamed when the illness persists, and the guilt is borne by the subject.) I called this chap, and told him that if indeed he had been healed of diabetes, it was the first such case in recorded history, and I would certainly include it in my book. He was very co-operative and gave me the name of his doctor. However, he warned me, that doctor would probably not admit that the healing had taken place – because he was 'not a Christian'. I was startled. What, I asked, would belief have to do with it? The man explained that his doctor had simply refused to accept this obvious miracle.

Then I began to suspect what was really going on. I asked him if he was still taking insulin, and he readily admitted that he was, but only because 'Satan has still some hold on me, so that I can't get up the courage and conviction to stop the medication.' Such redefining of goals and reality is typical of those who agree to play this game, a game they always lose.

The result of my book was that two of those I investigated went out of business (one has since started up again) and two of them went to prison. One healer I exposed on a major American TV show was at that time bringing in $4.3 million per month, and that was tax-free!

In the name of God

Several religious sects base their entire philosophy on methods of healing in which they choose to believe simply because such a belief satisfies their idea of how an ideal world should operate. But we are not living in an ideal world, and when the healing powers they preach are examined dispassionately, it is found that the 'cure rate' experienced by their followers is no higher than that of persons who receive no treatment whatever, and often much less. A recent US survey of college students showed a significantly lower life expectancy for those who attended Christian Science schools than for those who did not. Faced by such revelations, these naive people choose to ignore reality and turn their back on further examination of their dogma. And they continue to die before their time, having rejected what medical science – an admittedly imperfect art – can and probably would do for them. Saddest of all is the realization that these people subject their children to these restrictions as well, often with crippling or fatal results.

Malfunctions of the human body will occur, and since earliest times much of our philosophical and scientific effort has been directed towards repairing bodily damage and trying to prevent the ravages of nature and

" Fools furnish Quacks with *Cases.*"

Quacks have long been derided by the cartoonists.

accident. When medicine fails to supply a satisfactory answer, as it still often does, other methods which often promise miraculous results are sought out.

A dangerous notion

If these alternative systems are of any value at all, they should be used. But there is a serious and possibly deadly side effect of such use, in that the victim may ignore or give up potentially helpful medical care in favour of the non-invasive cures promised by the other systems. I heard one faith healer declare to his congregation, 'Jesus doesn't want to cut your body with steel knives, stick needles into you or put artificial chemicals into your body!' This kind of statement, obviously intended to bias the listener against medical science, appeals to many people who would rather have amulets, incantations, massages or manipulations of a more pleasant or more exotic and fashionable nature applied to their afflicted persons. Medical quacks have flourished on the basis of what they call the only 'real' evidence for their efficacy: the anecdotal testimonials supporting their work. I have heard such testimonials given in convincing tones by victims who, a few days later when I went to interview them, were dead of the diseases they had declared routed by the quack. You may recall that the actor Steve McQueen recorded and broadcast just such an affidavit only a few hours before he died in a Mexican quack's clinic.

The most important question
Of all the subjects that we dealt with in making *James Randi: Psychic Investigator*, faith healing and similar dubious alternatives to medical treatment seemed to us far the most important. Many 'psychics' who do the usual ESP, 'reading', prophecy and clairvoyance stunts eventually turn to claims of healing powers, obviously because it can bring them a much improved income, while they are thoroughly protected under the present laws of the UK.

The would-be physician
A 'healer' we did examine on that programme was Stephen Turoff. He runs a healing business in Danbury, Essex. Turoff says that when he begins his 'healing' process, he goes into a trance and his body is taken over by the spirit of a long-dead German doctor named Kahn, who is now apparently 126 years old. His brochure states that 'Mr Turoff offers both contact healing and psychic surgery, a unique form of healing which utilizes de-materialization of matter or a build-up of ectoplasm or electro-magnetic alterations whichever is appropriate for the patient.' It ends by assuring the customer that he is 'always in the hands of the healer and his inspired wisdom'.

The conditions under which Turoff performs his work frighten me. For a start, he has no evidence whatever that any person or doctor named Kahn has ever lived, in Germany or anywhere else. He is also visited, he says, by the spirit of 'Professor Faffy', who practised in London in the 1950s. Similarly, Turoff knows of no evidence for Faffy's existence. The supposed 'Dr Kahn' will not tell anyone when nor where he was born, so we could not determine whether or not he existed in real life, or simply as an invention of Turoff's which had the effect of adding flavour to his performance.

Turoff admits that he has no medical training, knowledge or ability whatsoever. He has never studied the subject. He also admits that he never uses any antiseptic procedures nor sterilizes any cutting or probing instruments. He confidently says that he can use contaminated or rusty instruments to invade his customers' bodies and no infection will occur.

An appalling demonstration
On our programme we showed our audience a shocking videotape, which had been made with Turoff's consent. Turoff, speaking in what he apparently believes to be a German accent, mimed the act of giving an 'injection' to a client with an imaginary syringe, then shoved a long pair of surgical forceps all the way up the person's nostril, certainly to the limit of

Professed healers such as Valentine Greatrakes, known as 'The Stroker', who worked in England in the seventeenth century, have amassed fortunes. He attributed all disease to evil spirits, and his method was simply to touch the afflicted.

the nasal passage, 5 inches (13 cm) or more. The discomfort experienced by the client was quite evident.

Next he performed what is known as 'wet cupping' on the back of a woman. This is a medieval procedure, once thought to be of value to promote bloodletting, when that process – now known to be not only useless but dangerous – was popular. It consisted of first making an incision with a knife, which Turoff did on the woman's back, without any sterilization, anaesthetic or antiseptic. He then put a bit of cotton wool soaked in alcohol on a coin, placed this near the cut, and ignited the alcohol. A small glass was then inverted over the site. At this point Turoff covered the area with a cloth, as if performing a conjuring trick, thus concealing from sight the process that now took place inside the inverted glass.

As the oxygen was consumed by the flame, a partial vacuum was naturally created, drawing the flesh up into the glass. This of course caused the wound to bleed, and when the partial vacuum was thus equalized, the cloth was removed so that one could see that about one-fifth of the volume of the glass was now filled with blood. This process could, to an uninformed person, appear as if some magical force had brought the blood from the wound. The blood was congealed, and Turoff announced that it was a clot of 'bad' blood.

The unfortunate woman on whom this act was performed was trembling violently during the cupping procedure, and it was all the filming crew could do not to intervene and stop it.

In the Granada studio, I had to apologize to my audience for any discomfort the videotape might have caused them, but we felt that they should actually see what was going on in Britain – and around the world – in the name of 'alternative medicine'. One gentleman in our audience, perhaps disturbed by the sight, fainted and was taken out.

A professional opinion

We had with us Dr Natalie MacDonald, Secretary of the Medical Ethics Community of the British Medical Association, who was distressed by what she had seen, but told us that there are no laws in the UK to require anyone to have any medical knowledge or training at all in order to practise what they regard as medicine. I found this incredible. But, even more astoundingly, no one may practise veterinary medicine without being licensed! I detect a warped sense of values here.

Dr MacDonald said that, since Stephen Turoff is not a registered medical practitioner, the BMA has no official interest nor authority in the matter, as it is an organization that regulates the conduct of doctors. It is, however, interesting to discover that the BMA is looking into the sanitary standards of the professional tattoo artists in Britain, and has expressed concern in that respect. Is it too much to ask that it might now turn its attention to amateur knife-wielders with medical pretensions, too?

During questioning before our cameras, Turoff adopted a secure, confident and authoritative attitude. That was not at all surprising, since he, a former carpenter, now finds himself wearing a bespoke suit and expensive watch, with a thriving business that requires no training, no skill, no insurance coverage and no fear that he might come under the threat of legal action.

A legal remedy?

Or is that quite true? It was suggested that a customer might be able to bring assault charges against Turoff. Professor Margot Brazier, of the Faculty of Law at Manchester University, agrees that there is a distinct possibility. But I rather doubt that any of his customers, who have displayed their naivety by putting himself in his hands, would be inclined to pursue such a remedy against Stephen Turoff. The fact is that he could cause facial paralysis by performing his forceps-up-the-nose routine; trained orthodox specialists have done this by accident when carrying out conventional sinus operations. More importantly, since he makes no effort to sterilize his instruments, Turoff is obviously a potential vector for deadly infections such as AIDS and hepatitis B, and many other diseases carried by blood or other body fluids.

Does someone have to die before anyone gets angry enough to put a stop to this? And does anyone care to answer this question? As for the 'possession' act that Turoff adopts, he seemed uncertain, both during the taping procedure at his place of business and in the studio, whether he was supposed to be Kahn or himself. Certainly Kahn was well aware of what travel arrangements Turoff's wife was supposed to be making for Turoff, when she asked him. But I suppose that's understandable: where one goes, so does the other.

The media seldom, if ever, make any attempts to check the claims they publish, and Stephen Turoff has received copious and very favourable press coverage. To editors, it seems, the story is the thing – true or not. By this means healers are publicized uncritically, and continue to flourish despite the fact that their abilities are not put to the test. Testimonials from selected people who 'feel better' after such treatment are not sufficient to excuse the media from the ethical burden of proof and investigation that, so far, most of them have effectively avoided.

Psychic surgery

Every week increasing numbers of people from all over the world arrive in Manila, capital of the Philippines, seeking magical aid from the *curanderos* who claim they can heal every sort of malady. Apparently by means of psychic – or divine – powers, these healers can reach their hands into the

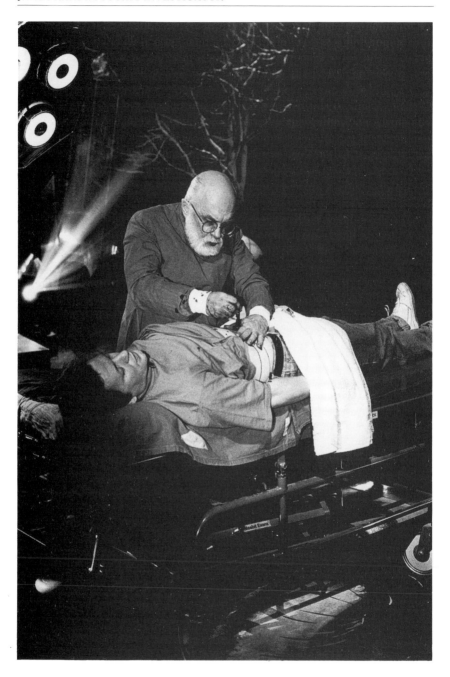

To the observer unfamiliar with the sleight of hand used here this demonstration of 'psychic surgery' appears very convincing.

bodies of their patients, extracting deadly tumours and other substances along with quantities of blood. In most cases there is no trace of an incision on the body of the patient afterwards.

To any trained conjuror, the methods by which these seeming miracles are produced are obvious. But inexperienced observers quite naturally do not see the trickery and, if they are predisposed to believe in magic, they are prepared to accept that something supernatural has taken place.

The genesis of the art

On an exploratory trip to Peru several years ago I made the acquaintance of a missionary named Joe Hocking, who lived and worked near a jungle town named Tingo Maria. While I am not much in favour of missionaries teaching native populations to be guilty of sin, I took to Joe and his wife, both dedicated people who were doing good things for those they had chosen to serve. The Hocking income came mostly from the sale of snake venom, which Joe harvested from unwilling and understandably angry fer-de-lance snakes before setting them free again. It is a job not without risk.

Aside from preaching the word to the locals, Joe Hocking was very active as a healer. His healing, though minor in scope, was real and effective. Unlike Turoff, Hocking used antiseptics and antibiotics, and he boiled his instruments. The endless parade of patients who queued up at his door during clinic hours displayed bites, minor abrasions, boils, rashes and dental problems for his attention. For the latter affliction extraction was the only remedy available to this devoted man, and he proudly displayed a huge bottle almost full of teeth he had pulled from grateful patients. To those who came by with the intention of making it a social obligation, 'Dr' Hocking solemnly passed out carefully selected aspirins of various colours, to the great and obvious satisfaction of the recipients.

A magic token is needed

My conversations with Joe revealed that the local people expected to see something actually removed from their bodies as symbolic of the removal of the cause of their problem. With the extraction of teeth, that requirement was obviously easily met, and in the few cases where bullets had been extracted both the practical and the symbolic needs had also been satisfied. But in the many other cases Joe Hocking had found that if he introduced a small stone or twig to the site of the operation, the patient expressed more contentment, since something had been produced that was identifiable as a cause of the discomfort. Anyone will forgive this minor deception. Though I am sure that Joe never quite realized it, he was involving a bit of 'show business' in his otherwise serious efforts to bring relief to the people he served.

I suspect that an anthropological study of this matter would conclude that Mr Hocking had independently discovered what is known in certain African societies as 'pulling the thorn'. This involves a similar surreptitious introduction to the site of the operation of a bit of thorn or sharp object, usually via the healer's mouth, since African procedures involve sucking the wound to remove the infection. This act, though obviously dangerous to both healer and patient from the infection point of view, might in some cases be very effective. The object is spat out and identified as the source of the evil. The satisfaction thus evoked enhances the reputation of the healer, who is usually performing useful minor medicine for people who have little if any other resource.

The process carried out in the Philippines may well have the same origins. There are two distinct classes of this performance, which is now known as 'psychic surgery'. The more common form is relatively free of direct and immediate physical damage or risk to the person treated. It consists of secretly transferring the blood and other materials to the surface of the body by means of sleight of hand. No incision takes place, and any infection which may occur is through minor abrasions or scratches. The second form of 'psychic surgery' is simply an invasion of the body by means of incisions, often made unobserved, under cover of distraction – in exactly the way that a conjuror would perform. Procedures such as 'cupping' – the same routine that Turoff uses – and the surreptitious introduction of small foreign bodies to the site of the incision are also often employed.

This Filipino practice has spread worldwide now, and in the state of Florida, where I live, psychic surgeons regularly visit on tour, untroubled by law enforcement agencies as they claim to be not medical doctors but priests, and so are protected by the principle of freedom of religion. Since actual incisions are seldom made, the risk of infection is small. These practitioners, often assuming the title 'Reverend' or 'Doctor', typically charge $100 per minute for their services. Some make no formal charge but accept sizeable 'donations' that are carefully suggested by them, in writing, to their customers.

A powerful documentary

In 1975 Granada TV produced an episode of *World In Action* that examined the claims of the Filipino psychic surgeons. It was certainly the most powerful and thorough coverage of that subject ever produced, with presenter Mike Scott graphically describing the frustration they experienced while trying to look into the fantastic claims made by the practitioners and, more importantly, recording the ecstatic endorsement of the victims, who were shown accepting every suggestion they were offered and believing that they had been healed of every sort of malady. The programme studied patients from Britain who had travelled to the

Philippines to be 'treated'. One died there, as did all the rest on their return except for one who merely went incurably blind.

The immense amount of money taken by the Filipino healers was made quite evident in the Granada film. It was shown that the healers had complete control of the hotels, restaurants and all other facilities that the victims used.

Oh no, not me!

It's easy for 'psychic healers' to point with derision at others in their trade and accuse them of all sorts of transgressions. In that way, they hope, they may be able to show that their own methods are not as dangerous or as bizarre as those of others. Most of these people also condemn orthodox medicine, pointing out that regular GPs make errors and cannot cure certain ailments. That's quite true; but orthodox medicine freely admits these failings, while the psychic healers confidently take on diseases which are known to be presently incurable, and by so doing quite possibly bring about infection, intensify illness and may even bring about their victims' death by steering them away from legitimate assistance.

I am sure that many of these psychic healers actually believe that they can heal. But they are not medically trained, they do not ascertain whether their patients actually have the diseases they complain of, they do not follow up their patients after treatment and, though they sometimes suggest that an orthodox GP should also be consulted (which avoids possible legal problems), they represent themselves as qualified to treat medical conditions, whether because they are in touch with disembodied spirits of some sort, or are prompted by extraterrestrial forces, or have been given a divine gift.

It is my view that all these claimed 'psychic healers' are potentially dangerous. There are, inevitably, cases where orthodox medicine has proven inadequate to certain challenges, and patients have been told that their condition is terminal. Is that sufficient reason to turn a blind eye to the psychic healers who then take over and promise a cure to these desperate persons? Consider the results of that false hope: continued expenditure by the patient and family, the heartbreak of the eventual realization that the euphoria was falsely based, and the final, justifiable anger at the healers who abused the trust that was so freely given to them.

No one is immune

The great comedian and actor Peter Sellers rejected the urgent advice of his physicians that he should undergo a heart bypass operation. He opted instead to visit the Filipino psychic surgeons, and they did their sleight of hand to his apparent satisfaction. Not surprisingly, his condition continued to deteriorate until he died, as his physicians had warned him. We are much the poorer for his loss, and the Filipino psychic surgeons are much richer.

Besides actors – intellectual giants such as Shirley MacLaine come to mind – many eminent people have chosen to believe that magic can cure them. Perhaps as a result of desperation, they clutch at this flimsy straw in the same way as would the less educated and less affluent. And they die in exactly the same way.

Medical science is not perfect. But, within its admitted limitations, it has produced virtual miracles of technology which support the lives of hundreds of thousands of human beings all over the world who would otherwise have died long before. The psychic healers have nothing but anecdotal, highly inflated accounts provided by those of their clients who survived – in spite of their dangerous intervention – diseases that either did not exist or would have got better anyway. Those clients who did not survive are no longer with us to express their dissatisfaction.

PSYCHOMETRY

Good and bad vibrations;
mostly bad.

CHAPTER 6

PSYCHOMETRY

He who has imagination without erudition
has wings while he lacks legs.
Joseph Joubert, 1754-1824

It is a common notion that 'psychic vibrations' – of some unspecified and undefined nature – can be absorbed by places and by objects, particularly objects made of metal. Many of us have had the experience of returning to a childhood location and feeling the 'chill' of returning memories from long ago. Standing before an ancient monument can bring us strange feelings that seem to be the result of the edifice itself, and not of our awareness of the history and the personalities involved with that monument. Who of us can walk through Westminster Abbey and fail to be stirred by memories of famous persons?

Certain people are said to have an ability to sense mysterious 'vibrations' taken up by objects from persons who have been associated with those objects in the past. This is called 'psychometry'. If it actually works it should be possible for a practitioner (a 'psychometrist') to 'read' vibrations from objects which have been intimately associated with a specific person, and to differentiate them from other similar objects owned by another person. And that's what we set out to test on our programme.

A tried method

I decided to use an excellent test that had been used in my 1989 TV special in the USA, *Exploring Psychic Powers: Live!* On that occasion I had asked our psychometrist to obtain vibrations from two different personal objects: we had used such things as wristwatches and keys (even more personal things such as false teeth might have been better, but there was the problem of embarrassment). In the British programme, we asked five gentlemen from our audience to contribute – temporarily, we assured them – their watches and keys. We mixed them together and presented them to our psychometrist, a London psychic named Petrene.

She was to sort through this selection of ten objects and attempting to match the watches with the appropriate keys. Now, if a gold Rolex watch were to show up in that selection, and also a key with a tag saying

'Rolls-Royce', our psychometrist would not have had much problem with matching those two. But that was unlikely, and it was equally unlikely that the owner of those keys and that watch would contribute them to us for this purpose!

If, as the psychometrists claim, a certain pattern of vibrations is absorbed by a person's watch, the same pattern should be retained by the keys that belong to the same person. A correct match should thus be obtained. The chance of matching all five pairs correctly by chance alone was one in 120. The likely chance result would be one in five. As usual, our subject expected to do better, claiming that powerful senses were at work.

I have tested this claimed ability many times without seeing any success so, when we drew up plans for doing this test on our programme in the UK, I was not expecting positive results. The psychometrist we chose, Petrene, is a professional psychic (£20 a reading) who claims this skill as well as an international reputation.

Not a very good start

As a demonstration of what she usually does, Petrene was asked to take an object from a stranger in the audience and do her regular reading on it. The first reading, done with a gentleman's wristwatch, was not very convincing, so she was asked to do another, this time with a gold ring, in the hope that it might be better. It was not, failing on nearly every count to identify with the lady owner. The better of the two readings was used for inclusion in the final edited programme.

We described to our audience the conditions of the keys-and-watch test. Though the matter had been discussed fully by telephone and the details had been worked out and agreed in advance of Petrene's appearance in our studio, when I introduced her on camera for the test she made a short speech to the effect that she had never done such a test before. She did agree, however, that it should be possible for psychometry to solve the problem.

The moment of truth

We presented Petrene with the ten objects, which had been meticulously isolated from one another to prevent any 'psychic contamination'. Carefully, she handled them and placed them in pairs in each of five sections of the table before her. We asked the five owners to come forward and each to stand behind the section in which his watch had been put, ignoring the keys for the moment. Then I asked each man to reach forward and push the keys away from the watch if the match was incorrect. Four of the five men did so. Petrene had scored exactly what might be expected by chance alone.

This result, one correct match out of five, was the same as we'd obtained in the previous show in the USA.

Objections from a PhD

One of the spectators in the audience was Dr David Cross, who holds a PhD degree in chemical oceanography from the University of Liverpool. He also runs a service called 'Ghost Bus Tours', which offers customers a visit to a haunted location, plus a three-course meal. The meal may well be the most rewarding part of the tour. He is also business manager for a 'psychic medium' named Jenny Bright, who was present as well. Jenny had originally been asked to be our psychometrist after she had answered our advertisement in *Psychic News*, but she had withdrawn late in the negotiations. In a letter sent to the producer of our programme following the taping, Dr Cross complained that 'bunches of keys from various sources will have several sets of vibrations connected with them, which is for the psychic . . . an almost impossible task. . . . Petrene certainly got full marks for putting herself "on the line", but zero for essentially agreeing to her own failure in advance.' With all due respect for Dr Cross's academic qualifications, I cannot see the validity of this criticism. I certainly have no keys on my own key chain that have ever belonged to anyone else, and I have carried them everywhere with me, so that they should be thoroughly saturated with my personal 'vibrations'. Also, we are told by the psychometrists that metal is an ideal substance for them to use. Furthermore, on several occasions in the past I have seen practitioners taking keys from audience members and obtaining what appeared to be excellent readings – though their seeming successes were, as usual, only the results of obtaining agreement from the subjects that certain suggested names and situations had been recognized.

I find the phrase 'agreeing to her own failure in advance' ill chosen. Petrene had agreed to the conditions of the test, had accepted that the sets of vibrations should be the same, and – most importantly – she was willing to accept success if it had been attained.

When I asked Dr Cross to suggest to me what he thought a fair test for psychometry might be, he replied that in his opinion it would be very difficult to put together a test that would be satisfying to 'both sides', as if a scientific experiment should or could have two 'sides'. A properly designed test has no preferred results, and no decision in advance – nor bias – is allowed to influence the design, conduct or reporting of the results. Such provisions must be written into any scientific test. The result must be accepted by all concerned. As I have said previously, if any claim is so vague, imprecise or ambiguous that it cannot be examined rationally, it cannot be tested and it cannot have the slightest importance or merit.

There is no doubt that the results of the test on Petrene were exactly the same as would have been expected from pure chance, as has been the case in all other proper tests of this claim that I have conducted.

The clearest possible test

Many years ago a Swiss psychologist named Zener designed a set of cards bearing five symbols which he felt were sufficiently different from one another to be ideal for conducting certain tests, among them ESP tests. These symbols are a circle, plus sign, wavy lines, square and star. Normally a deck of 25 cards is used, five of each symbol.

For decades these cards have been employed in parapsychological laboratories in the search for the ever elusive powers of telepathy and clairvoyance. So far, in spite of millions of pieces of data gathered through that extensive exploration, parapsychology has failed to yield convincing results.

One of the most important features of a true scientific experiment is that its results should be replicable: if the test is repeated in identical conditions, the results should be similar after allowing for the effects of chance. Tests with Zener cards have often shown runs of 'good' results, much as a roulette ball has been known to stop on red twenty times running; but it has never been possible to repeat such results consistently.

Despite the simplicity and obvious fairness of the Zener cards, wishful thinking and data searching (looking for and selecting positive data and omitting negative results, or both) invaded the labs of the paranormalists, giving further headaches to responsible, serious researchers who honestly wanted good data to be gathered, positive or negative. At present there is no replicated positive data available to support paranormal claims.

I have often given demonstrations of apparently paranormal effects, done by sleight of hand as I freely admit, and repeatable at will; but that is another thing entirely. Replication by conjurors of such wonders as spoon bending, clairvoyance, precognition, psychokinesis and levitation cannot prove anything about claims of real paranormal performance – except that it can easily be done by trickery. An audience of average intelligence and average powers of observation can usually be deceived.

The onus of proof is on Dr Cross and the other believers to establish their case, without resorting to special pleading and exceptions to standard expectations of scientific rigour. Conjurors often agree to the most stringent scientific restrictions, and still succeed in their performances. Yet they are only entertainers, bringing delight to the public, not leading them to believe the impossible, nor needing to prove anything. Conjuring is an ancient and honoured profession, and I'm proud to be involved in it.

The police psychics

Psychometrists often specialize. Some tell us they can handle items connected with crimes, particularly violent crimes, and can obtain impressions that help the police in the solutions of these crimes. These people are occasionally called in by the police, but more often it turns out that they themselves have contacted the police, saying that they know something about a crime, and are thus invited to make a statement. The police, by the very nature of their duties, must choose to record any volunteered information.

I have already mentioned Mr McGuire's claims about the 'Hillside Strangler'; in that case, whatever actually happened, the police took no notice of him. But in another case in the USA a few years ago, police listened with great interest to a psychic who ran on and on about a serious industrial fire that he had not only predicted with great accuracy, but about which he supplied important details after the event which, it appeared, he could know only through his special powers. His account was so accurate that he was immediately arrested, and an investigation soon revealed that he'd had no need of paranormal powers to produce his visions. His information was essentially first-hand: he himself had started the fire!

If a psychic demonstrates any ability to supply law enforcement officials with data which may help to solve a crime, that ability should be cultivated and used. The question is: Does such a power exist? To find out, American psychologist Dr Martin Reiser conducted two extensive investigations into the use of psychics by the Los Angeles Police Department. After several years of research, his conclusion was that psychics could contribute nothing useful to police work. 'Psychics come out of the woodwork during cases which the media become heavily involved in,' he said.

Part of Reiser's experimentation involved weapons used in homicide cases. These were mixed in with innocent items as controls, and it was found that the psychics were unable to differentiate between them. For our TV series we decided to employ methods similar to those that had been used by Dr Reiser.

Nella Jones

One very famous so-called 'police psychic' in the UK is Nella Jones, and we asked her to appear on *James Randi: Psychic Investigator* to answer a few questions about her work, and to demonstrate for us, with some rather fearsome artefacts, how she evaluates these objects for the police. At first the lady refused to appear on the programme with me, but after some coaxing she acquiesced. Some police officers at first agreed to appear with her, but eventually declined.

I asked Ms Jones what sort of information she could develop from merely handling such things as a victim's clothing and a murder weapon. Since she was about to 'psychometrize' possible murder weapons before a nationwide TV audience, she was cautious, and her answer did not include any definite assurance that she could develop anything. Instead, she rambled on vaguely about 'feelings' and such.

And how accurate was the information expected to be? Could we expect her to give dates and names? Oh, no. We'd just have to wait and see. I asked her whether there might be a danger that she could give information to the police of such a nature that an innocent person might be implicated in a crime. I was assured that such a possibility was not to be considered.

I then presented Ms Jones with six objects, telling her, 'Any or all of [these] could have been connected with a serious crime involving a loss of life. A history of each of these artefacts is known. They have been individually wrapped until now, to avoid the possibility of "psychic contamination".'

Nella Jones shuffled the six objects about, sealed in their individual plastic bags, then opened them. She selected a 'waiter's helper' (a jack-knife device with a short blade, a corkscrew and a bottle opener), a carpenter's hammer and a fireman's hand axe. She felt each of them carefully, and made her findings known. The waiter's helper, she said, might have been used to open a lock, the hammer might have been used to break a glass window to gain entry, and the axe might have been used to puncture a vehicle tyre. She failed to obtain specific readings on any of the other three items.

I asked Nella if she had anything more to say about the items she had chosen. She had, after all, been asked to identify which, if any, of the items might have been involved in a homicide.

I then opened the sealed statement and read to her and our audience the documentation on the objects she had chosen:

'Waiter's helper' folding bar utensil, made in Italy, purchased in Manchester, February 1991 by James Randi. Unused for any purpose. History: Direct from factory to retailer to purchaser.

Carpenter's hammer, purchased in Manchester, February 1991 by James Randi. Unused for any purpose. History: Direct from factory to retailer to purchaser.

Hand axe, of the type employed by firemen. In October of 1979, in Manchester, two men and a woman murdered Mr John Monk with this axe. They were tried on May 16, 1980 at Manchester Crown Court, found guilty, and sentenced to life imprisonment.

The system

I should like to point out that we had chosen the objects with great care. The purchases of all the innocent items for use as 'controls' in this experiment were documented by dated, printed receipts. All had been purchased from shops, and had not been handled or used for any purpose by anyone other than those involved in their manufacture, packing, shipping or retailing. They were not taken from a display in the shop, but were selected directly from stock. To obtain the murder weapon, we had the co-operation of the Museum of the Manchester Police Department, and the curator, Mr Duncan Brodie, was only able to supply us with one appropriate weapon. I took it from him sealed in a plastic bag, and it was thus presented to Nella, along with the other control items. The lettered tags on these artefacts had been attached in the order in which the artefacts were received. Complete histories of all these items were available upon request.

The murder axe had a particularly gruesome history. The two male murderers had plotted to entice their victim into the woman's bed. While he was preoccupied with other matters they had attacked him with the axe. They hacked him to death, then made an abortive attempt to dismember him with the axe. This bloody connection, I believe, police psychic Nella Jones should easily have been able to pick up if she indeed had any psychic powers.

Psychic News strikes again

Following Ms Jones's appearance on our programme, that ever eager promoter of miracles *Psychic News*, without troubling to check with us, quoted Nella's account of events.

She said she had only been given one minute to develop her psychic impressions of the items presented to her on the programme. (Not so: she took four minutes and thirty-one seconds, and was asked at the conclusion if she had anything more she wanted to add. Nella was not in any way restricted in the time allowed for her reading.)

She said she had been presented with twelve objects. (Wrong. There were only six.)

She said she had chosen only two out of the twelve, the hammer and the axe. (Actually, she chose three out of the six.)

She said that we later 'confirmed' that the axe had been used to murder two people in Germany. (No, no and no. There was nothing to confirm: we told her it was a murder weapon when she failed to identify it as such. Only one person was murdered, and the killing took place in Manchester, not in Germany.)

Nella said that on that programme, I performed a 'reconstruction [*sic*] of a spiritualist materialization, producing fake ectoplasm'. (Nella was obviously in a different studio. I did no such thing.)

She said, 'I didn't get time to go into details about the murder.' (Quite true, because she didn't know the axe was a murder weapon in the first place and she knew nothing about any murder!)

Furthermore, Nella Jones told our researcher that any moment now she is about to be declared an official police psychic, and she told us that New Scotland Yard had validated her claim that she was instrumental in assisting them to solve certain cases. She said we could check that. Well, we did check it, and we were told by Inspector Edward Ellison of the Yard that they never approach psychics for information; there are no official police psychics; they do not endorse psychics in any way; and there is no recorded instance of any psychic solving a criminal case or providing evidence or information that led directly to its solution.

Inspector Ellison told me that Nella had visited him after the TV taping, bending his ear for quite a while. 'The problem is,' said Ellison, 'that she can't accept my impartiality in the matter. We just don't have a policy regarding psychics.' There was at that very time, he told me, a year-long open-ended inquiry going on in his department to find out if any police officers consult psychics or are able to benefit from the use of psychics. In all of the eight districts of London that the Yard covers, he put out the word, and he found that rather than the officers seeking out the psychics, it's the other way around. As he put it, 'They've been approached, is the answer.'

'I've had a psychologist and a statistician standing by since last August, and so far, nothing reported,' said the Inspector. The inquiry will end in August, 1991. Before we said goodbye, Inspector Ellison shared a last anecdote with me. He was called by 'a young psychic' who ventured to tell him about a project he was currently involved in. He thinks there are several possible ways that could have been done, but one other thing she tried really impressed him. 'She said she could call my star sign,' he said, 'and she got it. On the eleventh guess.' That bad a miss really is impressive, I agree.

A real circus for psychics

The Yorkshire Ripper case was a bonanza for the UK psychics, and for the sensational newspapers as well. The *Sunday People* asked Britain's leading psychic at the time, Doris Stokes (who is now dead), what the Ripper looked like. Assisted by their staff artist, Doris produced the likeness shown here, said that his name was Johnny or Ronnie, and declared that he lived in Tyneside or Wearside.

Later, the *Daily Star* joined the circus by consulting an unnamed medium who provided psychic drawings of the Ripper's friends, relatives and even his car mechanic. Needless to say, all this information was not only useless but totally wrong.

It's no puzzle why the newspapers insist on perpetuating this foolishness, when the police themselves have no use for it. It sells papers; it's a good story, true or not. You won't read in the newspapers this remark made by Bob Baxter, Chief Press Officer for the West Yorkshire Police, who gave us a statement about the hundreds of persons who offered clues: 'Many people contacted us during the Ripper inquiry. Many of them were mediums or people professing to have psychic powers. However, nothing that any of these people told us has any bearing on the outcome of the case. We certainly did not discuss our investigations with them.'

Doris Stokes's 'psychic portrait' of the Yorkshire Ripper, drawn under her
guidance by a newspaper artist.

Taking advantage of grief

One famous disappearance case was that of Suzy Lamplugh, who has been
sought since 1986. Investigators were told by one psychic – who, I was
told, lost the way while trying to visit Suzy's mother! – that Putney Bridge
was somehow involved in the mystery, but that notion proved useless to
them. Psychic Doris Stokes said that Suzy was alive, as did most of the
psychics early on in the case; but then, when it began to appear unsolvable,
they began to say that she was dead.

How many psychics offered their ideas for locating Suzy? Some four
hundred of them. And what has been the result? Nothing at all. In response
to the psychics' instructions, much digging and probing has taken place,
but to no avail. When we spoke to a friend of the Lamplugh family on our
programme, she told us that an area the size of Chelsea Harbour could have
been dug up by now, with all the excavating that was done in response to
the psychics' urgings. She showed us two heavy suitcases that she'd brought
along with her to the TV studio for our show, filled with letters from all
those psychics who had offered ideas to solve the case. None were of any
use.

Also present was Mrs Christine Boxell, whose young son Lee vanished on
10 September 1988. Again, as with the Lamplughs, a horde of psychics had
written to and rung the Boxell family. One insisted that Lee was to be found
in Slough, and both parents went there to put up 'Have you seen . . .'

posters everywhere. There was no response. We asked what the psychics had done for her, and the results were the same. They were of no help whatever, and they wasted a lot of valuable time and effort.

Are any of the psychics right in any of these cases? Probably at least one of them is. With so many thousands of statements having been made, it's almost certain that one of this multitude of persons must have made a couple of correct guesses. You can depend upon it: should either of these two cases be solved tomorrow, one or more psychics will then come forward and claim success. The others – and their statements – will be forgotten.

Spirit portraits

Coral Polge, who makes her living by producing pastel portraits of people whom she vaguely defines as 'entities', was featured on one of our programmes. She says that she is guided by the spirit of Maurice de la Tour (also known as Maurice San Quentin, she tells us). Before the cameras Ms Polge skilfully drew, in brown chalk, the face of a middle-aged, rather ordinary lady that I think could be any one of a half-dozen such women that the average person has encountered at one time or another. However, despite the earnest efforts of her assistant and cheerleader Stephen O'Brien to encourage any audience member to identify with this ephemeral lady, there were no takers.

(Mr O'Brien has made the astonishing claim that he answers an average of one letter every ten minutes for his clients, every week, over a six-day working week, which made us all the more grateful that he could take the time to appear on our programme.)

As we continued the taping it became clear that Stephen himself was doing quite well with a gentleman in the back row, who said that he could 'accept' several names and situations that O'Brien was coming up with, but not, unfortunately, in connection with the Brown Lady that Coral was retouching vigorously in the background.

I thought there was something vaguely familiar about this chap who was apparently rescuing the situation, at least as far as O'Brien was concerned. Later we were to learn who he was.

An unforeseen change of plans

As we progressed with the programme tapings of *James Randi: Psychic Investigator*, it became evident that some of the claimants – and some of the invited guests – intended to give us less than they had promised us. Also, they tended to abandon previously decided rules and limits, changing what we had agreed on at the very last moment. In the case of Coral Polge, our researchers had firmly agreed with her that she could and would produce a sketch within five minutes. However, as she and O'Brien stepped before the cameras, it was announced that she now required ten minutes. A hasty conference in the control room resulted in a reluctant assent to this expensive and awkward change, and the two performers started. After just over ten minutes, I had to walk on the set and attempted to stop O'Brien. He insisted on continuing, since he had only just started talking with that mysterious man in the back row, from whom he seemed to be getting so much agreement. Out of simple courtesy we allowed him to continue for another minute, then we simply stopped taping to clear the set for the next scene. We had been shown no courtesy in the matter at all.

A minor mystery solved

And who was that man in the back row? Had I seen him on a television programme? That same thought had occurred to two of my friends who were in that audience, and they also thought they had recognized him. It was no great surprise to us to discover after the taping that the gentleman was himself a professional spirit medium. This may have had some bearing on what was going on.

In any case, no one in the audience of ninety people was able to identify both with the portrait that Coral Polge drew and the description that she offered. However, when I asked for a vote on whether anyone could recognize the face, the response was 11 per cent! No two people should have recognized that person, unless they had both known her. It was the unspecific nature of the drawing that had caused so many to find the face familiar, and the scenario Polge and O'Brien were trying to build – that of a distinct person 'coming through' for a specific member of the audience – was not at all established. In any case, Coral Polge had told us before the reading that only one person should relate to the drawing.

Starting from cold

Among practitioners of the occult arts there is a technique known as 'cold reading'. When the artist is faced with an audience that is entirely strange to him he uses tried-and-true methods of guessing names, relationships, events and situations that might relate to audience members.

That is in contrast to 'hot reading', which is used when the reader has obtained specific, hard information about a sitter, and merely has to reveal it in a convincing manner. British author and historian Ian Wilson looked into Doris Stokes's methods, and discovered that the people for whom she had produced 'evidential' messages had contacted her in advance of the show and given her information, and had then been invited to attend her meeting. The information she'd received from them was then given back to them and embellished upon. Ms Stokes's work serves well as an example of 'hot reading'.

Performing cold reading by throwing out common names and hoping that someone will 'link' with one of them, then guessing or simply asking the relationship of a name that has been selected out and 'accepted' by a sitter, the medium is well on the way to convincing an unwary listener that he has contacted the dead.

But look at the way it's done. Suppose a sitter has accepted the name 'Mary'. The medium can now say, 'I want to put Mary close to you.' What does this really mean? It's really a question as to whether or not Mary is 'close to' the sitter. In the worst-case scenario, where Mary is dead, is buried in another country, was never very fond of the sitter and was not related to him, we might uncharitably fail to recognize how close that guess was. However, a clever medium can easily rescue this seeming bad guess by saying, 'Ah, but though Mary failed to tell you of her great affection for you while she was here, she has come through tonight to remedy all that.' Though it sounds hard to believe, naive sitters actually accept such excuses. They want to.

American magician Harry Houdini, at one seance in which he tried to establish contact with his deceased mother, was astonished to hear her speaking English, a tongue she never used. The medium, true to her calling, was unfazed. 'In Heaven,' she reported, 'everyone speaks English.' Though this did not convince Houdini, and I don't particularly expect to visit the celestial kingdom after my demise, it is reassuring to know that the language of Shakespeare will be used in daily affairs.

The cold reading routine includes a number of excellent methods for extracting information from the sitter without it appearing that the medium has actually asked for it. Comments such as 'Why is this person laughing?' or 'She's shaking her head as if to say no' will often elicit a response. Some questions don't appear to be questions at all: 'I get this person in spirit' or 'Somehow, I feel Jim was related to you, or lived near you' are examples. Even more useful are those modifiers that generalize or fuzz up the statement so that it has a greater chance of being successful or of evoking an answer. Phrases like 'I think that . . .', 'I feel as if . . .', 'I want to say . . .' and many other 'try-ons' are used for this purpose.

There are other useful gimmicks. Say, 'Yes, of course,' and then repeat to the sitter a fact that he has just given you, as if you knew it all along. Say, 'Of course, I got that very strongly!' when he gives you a fact that you didn't get at all. When you hear something from the sitter that appears to 'link' with the line you are shooting, declare, 'Now we're putting it all together,' even though he is the one who is making it work.

Where do they learn the act?

Cold reading isn't necessarily learnt in a series of lessons. Though the classes in 'spiritual development' that medium Maureen Flynn conducts are obviously intended, both by teacher and students, to enhance their awareness of some vague survival-after-death philosophy, the lessons seem

One spirit medium of the 1920s was Anna Clark Benninghofer, who revealed to Harry Houdini her secrets of the 'dark seances' where she produced disembodied voices. Here they are seen with a 'spirit trumpet', once a mediums' prop.

also to instruct the learners to extract certainty from ambiguity. Trying to sense a word sealed in an envelope, students are encouraged to discover relationships between obscure ramblings and the word itself. A notion about walking down a road, for example, is said to correctly relate to the concealed word 'success' because 'everyone seeks a path to success, and a path is a sort of road.' The words used are always general in nature (success, peace, happiness, sadness, longing, searching) rather than more definite terms like cat, house, Germany, or coffee.

Most mastery of cold reading is obtained by observing old masters – such as the late Doris Stokes – and by trial and error. The methods of probing and backing up, laughing away failures and turning them into forgivable slips, getting around long pauses in which the sitter fails to volunteer needed information, and blaming errors on the poor spiritual wavelengths all become clear with a little study.

This 1887 illustration shows what sistters in the dark-room seance imagined to be happening, as ghostly music was heard from mid-air and writing was found upon a sheet of paper or a slate when the lights went up again.

When all else fails . . .

True to form, Stephen O'Brien admonished the audience at the close of his reading for us that it had all been just an 'experiment'. Mind you, when a successful series of apparently 'evidential' links has been achieved, such an admonition is not offered; in that case, contact with a departed person is said to have been firmly established. Stephen told the audience that they should all go home, do some research and try hard to think of some link with this Brown Lady. In the several shows I've see O'Brien do, he has never failed to ask the subject to go home and try to come up with something that might save his misses.

Following an appearance on the *Wogan* programme in March 1991, Mr O'Brien used that same plea for 'research' to establish any connections for an avalanche of guesses he launched at an amused lady in the studio audience. Every one of his guesses failed to hit home, even though they were the very best of his cold reading repertoire.

Psychic News, never missing an opportunity to be wrong, reported that O'Brien's failure during his appearance on *Wogan* was attributable to his failing to notice a lady for whom the reading was actually intended, and was wildly waving in the background to attract his attention. Wogan's staff looked at the tape and reported that the lady in question was merely patting her hair into place.

Get a connection — any connection

That's what it's really all about. The victims of such flummery are encouraged to think of something that can link the banal but tried-and-true phrases to any person or situation they can come up with. The vague language and the inevitable modifiers often offer many easy connections.

Consider some of the phrases that were used in the Coral Polge-Stephen O'Brien reading. The items marked with an asterisk were 'accepted' by someone in the audience.

Terribly short of breath
Heart trouble
Chest condition
Thick hair (thinned out later in life)
Angina
Passed peacefully
War years
Butler*
William
Passed several years ago
Bombed in World War 2
Three sisters*
Manual work

Uncle Tom*
Something wrong with one leg*
Knee
Move of house

Generally, the phrases were separated by such things as:

I want to say that . . .
I feel that . . .
Possibly . . .
It might be that . . .
I'm led to say that . . .
I get the feeling that . . .
I'm being told that . . .
Why do I say that . . .
Why do I feel that . . .

How *Psychic News* sees things

In *Psychic News* two weeks after the taping, under the front-page headline 'Medium says filming for TV was a farce', Ms Polge described the studio episode in which she demonstrated her talents for us as 'a farce' and 'ridiculous'. I wouldn't disagree. She also told the paper that the mother of Suzy Lamplugh was in our studio; she was not.

Psychic News is the newspaper that ran another front-page story in 1975 describing a marvellous 'psychic' who had visited their offices. According to their awestruck reporter, everything in sight was bent by his powers.

[The psychic] seemed to radiate a magnetic aura. . . . I collected a teaspoon. . . . I touched the spoon ends as he stroked it. Suddenly it seemed to shudder. Then it broke cleanly in two. . . . We found the occupants [of the office] excitedly proclaiming, 'Look at the paper knife.' Lillian had used it that morning to open the mail. It was perfectly straight then. Now its handle had curved up an astonishing 45 degrees. All could vouch [the psychic] had not been near it. Up to that point he had not entered their office. Later [another employee] announced, 'My teaspoon has bent!' It was perfect when she stirred the tea a few moments earlier. . . . [An employee] noticed her clock had suddenly gained two hours. It had been correct earlier. A glance at my office clock showed it fast by 2½ hours! Certainly [the psychic] had no opportunity to interfere with them. He had been under constant surveillance. I had not left his side, or taken my eyes from him, for one second. I was determined to be an objective reporter. I was fully alert to any suspicious moves. But [he] made none. At one stage he stroked a fork. He seemed unable to make any impression. But after he left I discovered it had twisted noticeably. [An employee] also found a filing cabinet key had bent in the lock.

This sensational article was complemented by a front-page photograph showing a strange individual, not without a certain weird charm, holding an array of bent cutlery.

Just what was going on here? If, as the reporter for *Psychic News* says, he 'had not left his side, or taken [his] eyes from him, for one second', we have here absolutely irrefutable evidence for psychokinetic power. Or maybe not. Though this was an experienced reporter, and this newspaper is noted for relating accounts of wondrous events to its enthralled readers, I must tell you that the 'psychic' was in that office for more than an hour, wandering about from room to room freely, physically bending everything that came to hand. The description given is exceedingly faulty and does not represent the facts of the matter at all; there was no surveillance at all, let alone a 'constant' surveillance.

The newspaper had been bamboozled by simple conjuring tricks that required little skill except some fast talk. The 'psychic' was myself.

Can it get much sillier?

Following a rehearsal of Coral Polge's part in our programme, we overheard her talking with some of the studio workers and showing them various portraits she'd done of 'spirit people'. It was hard to suppress a chuckle when she indicated one drawing she'd done of a young lad 'three years before he was born'. I challenge you to accept that.

READING BETWEEN THE LINES

Dot your 'i's and cross
your 't's. Or you're sacked.

CHAPTER 7

READING BETWEEN THE LINES

It is the sign of a trifling character
to catch at fame that is got by silly reports.
Cicero, 106-43 BC

An impressive gentleman named Duncan McIntosh had agreed to appear on the *James Randi: Psychic Investigator* series to demonstrate under test conditions that graphology, an art he professionally pursues on behalf of important industrial and government agencies, can be used to decide whether people are suited for employment in certain professions. Mr McIntosh gave us a list of the five callings that he felt were particularly well indicated in handwriting patterns. We were asked to obtain writing samples from each of five individuals in those professions – computer specialist, secretary, artist, farmer and salesperson.

Mr McIntosh gave us an important warning. He told us that 85 per cent of people are not in the work for which they are best suited, which seemed to me a very convenient 'out' if his decisions were wrong. For that reason our researchers obtained five women who declared, under careful questioning, that they were truly happy in their chosen professions.

Their handwriting samples were presented to Mr McIntosh early on the afternoon of the taping, so that he could have plenty of time to make his decision. He was required to match all five of the samples to their respective professions, a task that had a chance of success of only one in 120, and an expectation that one would be correctly matched to the five subjects if chance alone were operating.

We presented the line-up of volunteers to Duncan and our audience, and I was struck, meeting these people for the first time, that for me it would have been impossible to guess to which professions they might be assigned. With one exception, that is. The woman who pursued farming was bursting with robust energy in a way that left no doubt at all of her calling. She was most impressive.

Mr McIntosh evidently had a different impression. In fact he was right in only one of his guesses – the artist, Lesley Hakim-Dowek. That one-in-five result was exactly in accordance with chance expectation, not to my surprise; and in any case, that sample of handwriting was pretty easy to guess, with its stylish flourishes.

As I said on that programme, I wonder how many persons have been accepted or rejected for employment on the strength of a graphological analysis performed for a prospective employer? Would you be willing to trust your future to this art? I know I would not.

During the announcement of his findings before our studio audience Duncan McIntosh told Morag Bell, the computer specialist (whom he had identified as a farmer), that she had a scar on her abdomen, a fact which he had apparently determined merely from examining her writing! Unfortunately for his theory, the lady denied his assertion, and we did not insist on further disclosure. Later, after the taping, when Duncan got to speak to her, it was found that she did have a scar on her leg, which prompted Duncan to claim that he knew she had a scar, but had merely mislocated it. Morag herself was perceptive enough to note that almost everyone has a scar somewhere. I certainly do.

That was far from my first exposure to this sort of craft. Some years ago, when I was presenter of an all-night radio programme in New York City, a famous graphologist, Nadya Olyanova, appeared on one of my discussion programmes. Before the show she asked me for a sample of my signature, and wanted to obtain one of the famous American escape artist Harry Houdini. I told her that I could supply both, and sent my secretary Micky to my apartment to get from my collection an autographed photo of Houdini. Micky was to photocopy the signature for use on that night's show; but she had no time to get to a photocopier, so she merely copied out the autograph, thereby changing it entirely in slant, style and formation.

When I showed up at the studio that night I saw the bogus Houdini autograph, along with mine, lying on the table. Recognizing that it was nothing like the real one, I left the studio to find Micky and told her off for being so careless. Then, as now, I could not afford to be accused of playing unfairly.

As we both returned to the studio I saw that Ms Olyanova had entered and was already studying the bogus signature. Curious, I waited to see what she would say about it, and sat transfixed as she averred that the writing revealed the owner's ability to extricate himself from physical situations, along with his knowledge of mechanical devices such as locks.

When the programme started a few minutes later I at once made it clear that I was highly doubtful of the graphologist's claims. She immediately became very defensive and said some pretty hard things to me. I had no chance to tell her about the inadvertent imposture that had occurred and, before I could do so, she left with both signatures in hand. I had no notion that she intended to make use of them.

Soon afterwards, as I understand, Ms Olyanova wrote a book which included both signatures along with her detailed analyses of them. My

A popular forger's trick is to duplicate a signature by 'drawing' it upside down. This actually produces a better forgery than doing it upright, since the artist's own handwriting variations are not involved and do not interfere with a proper copying of the original.

'reading' was quite unflattering, which may be valid; while that of Houdini's – or rather, Micky's – handwriting glowed with marvellous revelations about show business and derring-do, along with references to his ability as an escape artist. Is it any wonder that I am sceptical about graphology?

The usual objections

The day after the videotaping with Duncan McIntosh, he telephoned to inform us that he had managed to interview each of the five women we had used in the test, and discovered that each of them had actually at one time been involved in the profession he'd assigned them to by his graphological analysis.

Willing to be convinced, our researchers sprang to their telephones and began asking about this. Jane Grant, the salesperson who had been guessed as a secretary by Duncan, had actually been a secretary at one time. But Morag Bell, the computer specialist, had also been a secretary, not an unlikely early occupation for women starting in business in Britain. As for being a farmer, as Duncan had averred, Morag denied that she had ever had the slightest interest in that pursuit, and certainly was never involved in it. Secretary Betty Kelly, who according to Duncan should have been a salesperson, told us that she was 'briefly' an Avon lady, but that the experience was, to her, 'insignificant'. And Margaret Wilkinson, the splendid lady who was supposed to be better off as a computer specialist than as a farmer, had always been a farmer since attending agricultural college, and came from a family of farmers. She had no ambition at all to become involved with computers.

Allow me to advise Duncan McIntosh, without even seeing his handwriting: judging from the results of these guesses, I suggest that he might consider not again subjecting his art to such a test.

In closing this subject I will quote John Beck, secretary of the National Society of Graphologists, who told us that there are 'only 4 or 5 true graphologists' in the UK. He did not say whether Duncan McIntosh was one of that select group. Says Beck, those few are so accurate that 'sometimes they can tell what a person had for breakfast that morning.' Graphology, he says, is 'the most precise of the "ologies", but has a problem in that '99 per cent of persons in the UK are not in the right jobs.' He also told us that graphology is a brand of psychology. If so, I will have to have another serious look at psychology.

Graphologists, in common with astrologers and other similar 'experts', can disagree. Mr Beck feels that Duncan is incorrect in saying that, for example, an open 'o' in handwriting signifies an open mouth, and thus a gabby person. Beck likes to think that it means 'curiosity and shyness'. This must indeed be a difficult art to master.

THROUGH A GLASS DARKLY

Que será, será,
Whatever will be, will be
The future's not ours to see . . .

CHAPTER 8

THROUGH A GLASS DARKLY

*The best guesser is always called
the most sagacious prophet.*
Cicero, 106-43 BC

Previous chapters have been mostly about my testing of the claims of mystics, psychics and the like. But of course there are many such people whose claims can hardly be tested on television. Chief among those are the numerous prophets of doom. I should now like to look at a few of these, past and present.

Like all branches of psychic whimsy, that of prophecy involves a parade of figures who bring things to life by their force of personality. Not infrequently persons who have achieved fame in other fields will suddenly 'flip out' and announce that they have been contacted by UFOs, spoken to by God or otherwise selected by hidden forces to bring enlightenment to the human race. Let's look at a few of these characters.

In important company

Just in time for April Fools' Day 1991, former Hereford United goalkeeper David Icke, also famous as a broadcaster and a spokesperson for the Green Party, threw off his cocoon and emerged as a turquoise-robed guru at a press conference which he had called to declare the following world-shaking events.

In Mr Icke's mystical vision, 'disruptive thought vibrations' originating with the Sicilian Mafia and the Tiananmen Square massacre have combined to set in motion a cataclysm that will first be evidenced when Mount Rainier in the USA explodes. This pyrotechnic display will be followed, said David, by the complete disappearance of New Zealand, the collapse of the Channel Tunnel, the fall of Naples Cathedral and an unspecified failure of the Texas oilfields. These misfortunes will be brought about by the dreaded archangel Ak-Taurus, who, he said, had previously managed to frustrate an attempt by the citizens of Atlantis (no doubt warned in vain by some other genius in a turquoise bathrobe) to avoid the submersion of that mighty civilization. The Atlanteans had been urged to tune in to the massive power point at Stonehenge to save themselves; but as we know, they all went under and property values there have never recovered.

And where did all this impressive data come from? David Icke has been in personal touch with Socrates, 'the Godhead', Jesus Christ and other all-time greats. They chose him to be the 'channel for the Christ spirit', so we'd better listen, especially since King Arthur and Merlin (they are also archangels, as no doubt you know) have turned off Stonehenge so that the beastly Ak-Taurus can't use it against us. That's some comfort, at least.

My attitude may lead Mr Icke to classify me as one of those people who 'vibrate at a lower thought level'. But I'm content to wait for Christmas 1991, when he has proclaimed that Cuba, Greece, the Isle of Arran, the cliffs of Kent, and Teesside will be hit by a monster earthquake (eight on the Richter scale) that will submerge them.

My own prediction, made without consulting the noted authorities Mr Icke quotes, is as follows. When the above events do not occur, David will give credit for our deliverance to his own intervention and to the mental energies of the coterie of loonies who will inevitably adhere to his robes and throw money to his cause. There is always a cluster of these waiting to leap into the lap of any guru.

It seems to me that in the case of David Icke there are only three possible scenarios:

1 Mr Icke may well believe that he has been divinely appointed to this position to save us all. He would not be the first to entertain such a belief. He would join many others, such as Joan of Arc, William Miller, John Brown, Joseph Smith and the Maharishi Mahesh Yogi, in that select band.

2 He may have launched the press event as an elaborate April Fools' Day hoax, which might not harm the reception of his new book, *The Truth Vibrations* which, the media were assured, would be published in May. By the time this book comes out I'm sure you'll have your copy.

3 Socrates and Jesus, having survived the hemlock and the Romans by being translated to another dimension, may really have appeared to David Icke so that we lesser mortals might be warned of exploding mountains, inundated nations and the other unpleasant happenings that he says are imminent.

I fear that the first of these is not unlikely, and I would not dismiss the second. The third I find less probable, so much so that I am actually flying in the face of Fate by making plans to visit New Zealand next year. If it's gone I'll let you know.

Nostradamus, after an illustration by his son, César.

The great seer

One of the most renowned presagers of disaster, whose fame has lasted to this day, was Michel de Notre-Dame, a physician born in Provence in 1503, and usually better known by the Latin form of his name, Nostradamus. His principal work was the *Centuries*, a series of almost a thousand quatrains which purported to be prophecies. With this and a great number of almanacs, letters and various other writings, he managed to produce more than any other prophet of history. His reputation, however, is due to the ardent horde of his disciples who continue to this day to hyperbolize, select and invent in order to perpetuate his fame.

Under the patronage and protection of Catherine de' Medici, queen of France and the power behind three French kings, Nostradamus lived comfortably till his death in 1566, celebrated all over Europe and a thorn in the side of Elizabeth I of England, for whom he continually predicted in his almanacs a doom which never came.

On close examination it can be seen that many of the quatrains penned by the seer of Provence were actually political commentaries and justifiable criticisms of the activities of the Catholic Church, then merrily tossing heretics onto bonfires wherever the Inquisition could reach. As I recently discovered, Nostradamus himself was in great danger of ending up in flames himself, since letters now in the Bibliothèque Nationale in Paris prove that he was a secret heretic – a Lutheran – and he was already under suspicion because only two generations earlier the Notre-Dames had been the Gassonets, a Jewish family that converted to Catholicism under pressure.

A good look at just one of the Nostradamus quatrains, one of the 'top ten' presented by his fans as evidence of his prophetic ability, will serve to illustrate how far believers will go to stretch the facts in order to serve their needs. Quatrain 51 of Century II is said by the faithful to refer to the Great Fire of London. Let's look at the evidence for this belief.

First, quoting from the earliest available (1558) edition of the verse, it reads:

> *Le sang du iuste à Londres fera faute,*
> *Bruslés par fouldres de vint trois les six:*
> *La dame antique cherra de place haute,*
> *De mesme secte plusieurs seront occis.*

A standard translation is:

> The blood of the just shall be wanting in London,
> Burnt by thunderbolts of twenty-three the six(es),
> The ancient dame shall fall from [her] high place,
> Of the same sect many shall be killed.

The word *faute* may equally well mean 'lack' or 'fault'. *Feu* (fire) is substituted for the original *fouldres* (thunderbolts) in the second line by many copyists, probably to make it better fit the Great Fire of London interpretation. Also some editions, for the same reason, print *vingt & trois* rather than *de vint trois*. Either might be read as 'twenty-three' or, by a stretch of the imagination, especially in the case of *vingt & trois*, which is not the usual form for 'twenty-three', as 'three twenties' or 'threescore', that is, sixty – which with the remaining number makes sixty-six. The Great Fire was in 1666.

The Nostradamians would ask us to believe that their hero was writing about an event that was 111 years in his future. The fire destroyed four-fifths of the city. It is said by one of the interpreters that the last half of line two refers to the number of houses and buildings that were burnt, rather than the more popular interpretation by almost everyone else that it means 66.

The Nostradamians go on to explain that *la dame antique* refers to Old St Paul's Cathedral, which was destroyed along with many other churches, thus making sense of the line 'Of the same sect many shall be killed.' St Paul's was never, as far as I have been able to determine, called 'The Old Lady' as claimed. Also, the word *antique* in the French of the day meant both 'old' and 'eccentric'. The derivation is similar to that of the English word 'antic'. Though Old St Paul's Cathedral had a notably tall spire, there is no 'high place' from which it could have fallen. Some fans, recognizing this discrepancy, claim that a statue of the Virgin Mary stood on top of St Paul's, and that it was the Old Lady that Nostradamus was referring to. Needless to say, there is no evidence for any such statue, even before the Protestants had stripped these from English churches.

At this point, we have left only the reference to London. The quatrain actually refers to an event which was taking place as Nostradamus was working in 1555, but a very different one from the later Great Fire. Here are the historical facts.

1 Announcing a purge of her kingdom in 1554, the ferociously Catholic queen 'Bloody' Mary I of England began executing Protestant heretics in London, beginning in January 1555. Many were prominent churchmen, intellectuals and statesmen.

2 The trial, sentencing and burning of these unfortunates began on 22 January 1555 (not quite 'twenty-three', but a near miss). They were dealt with in neat groups of six. When they eventually expired at the stake, it was with a spectacular explosion, like a thunderbolt, since they were burnt with the 'merciful' addition of bags of gunpowder tied between their legs or around their necks to quicken their passage. Bishop Nicholas Ridley met an especially horrible end. His brother-in-law, wishing to lessen his relative's suffering by hastening his death, had piled the faggots so high about him that the flames could not reach the gunpowder, and the poor man cried out that he could not burn. His benefactor thereupon opened up the pile of wood, so that the powder ignited and brought an end to the ordeal.

3 Mary, totally obsessed with religion, disappointed in love, ill with dropsy and several other diseases, repeatedly imagined that she was pregnant by her husband Philip of Spain. He was seldom at home and in 1555 left England and Mary for good. She wandered about her palace half naked while the atrocities were being committed in her name. She died three years later, incoherent and considered quite insane. It was strongly suspected that her exit was hastened.

4 Over 300 Protestants were executed in this way at that time.

I ask you to consider these historical facts, and compare them line for line and number for number with the four lines of the Nostradamus quatrain as seen in this much better translation:

1 The blood of the innocent will be a fault at London,
2 Burnt by thunderbolts, of twenty-three, the six(es),
3 The senile lady will lose her high position,
4 Many more of the same sect will be slain.

An important question arises here. Did Nostradamus have time to get this event into his publication? The first edition of the *Centuries*, in which this quatrain is printed, is dated 4 May 1555 – more than three months after the first group of heretics mounted the faggots in London. (There is even a case to be made that the actual first printing was in 1558, and that the 1555 edition never existed.) Though some authorities date the 1555 edition of the *Centuries* to 1 March 1555, it states plainly at the end of the book: *Ce present livre a esté achevé d'imprimer le IIII. iour de may M.DLV* ('This book finished printing the fourth day of May 1555').

The sentences of the inevitable executions would have been passed some time before the events, since the condemned often spent many months in prison while their wealth was found and seized by the Crown; carefully applied and controlled torture effectively extracted information from the condemned about concealed assets. Nostradamus was part of a network of scholars who were in frequent communication, and would have heard of this event. Thus either publication date is adequate for the described scenario.

Despite Nostradamus' public profession of being a faithful Catholic, who should have approved of the good work of burning heretics, he was, as we now know, secretly a heretic himself, a Lutheran sympathizer who declared himself in clandestine letters sent to clients and scholars in Germany. I believe that in this quatrain, as in many others, the Seer of Provence was writing in veiled terms of something he could not have condemned openly. In any case the executions would certainly have been hot news in France.

The prophecies of Nostradamus will surely continue to titillate the public for many more generations. His end-of-the-world alarms (1999 is one) will always stir editors to excesses of hyperbole and invention, and readers will dutifully fall in line. If in 1991 a seventy-two-year-old American climatologist named Iben Browning can cause shops to sell out of metal strapping and tinned food, and schools to close down, on the strength of an earthquake prediction based on incorrect astronomical calculations, surely a prophet who made his calculations in Provence four centuries ago will bring a certain amount of fear into some hearts. I also recall that 21 per cent of Americans questioned in a recent survey believe that the Sun circles the Earth.

Except for my concern about educational standards, I'm not losing much sleep, either about earthquakes or about the end of the world.

Dr Dee, sorcerer to Elizabeth I

Prophecy and other supernatural abilities were attributed to a contemporary of Nostradamus, Welshman Dr John Dee, who was born in 1527. He was many things: mathematician, navigator, cartographer, prolific writer, master spy, sorcerer, astrologer and most trusted adviser to Queen Elizabeth I of England. A tall, thin, mysterious man with a long, pointed beard, Dee was one of the most powerful but subtle political influences of his day. A genuinely accomplished scholar who was never reluctant to mix a little attractive claptrap in with his otherwise valuable teachings, he was, it is believed, the model for Shakespeare's character Prospero in *The Tempest*.

Dee dabbled in the magical arts from the beginning of his career, and at first was known only as a sorcerer. Before Elizabeth Tudor ascended the throne, and while she was a reluctant resident of the Tower of London, he predicted for her a very long life and a very high position in the kingdom (a most successful prophecy!). From that moment on he enjoyed her trust and her considerable patronage.

In spite of a certain dismay over his open association with acknowledged rogues and rumoured practitioners of the Black Arts, the Virgin Queen appointed him to ever more important positions.

Elizabeth valued above all his purported ability to predict the future. Some of Dee's magical paraphernalia is still preserved in London at the British Museum, and the most prized object on display is a magic obsidian (black volcanic glass) mirror 7 inches (18 cm) in diameter fashioned in Mexico by the Aztecs. In it, Dee claimed he could see future events by what

Dr John Dee consults the crystal ball, watched by his assistant Kelley.

is known as 'scrying'. This is done by looking into a bowl of water, a crystal or – as in Dee's case – a special mirror. Surprisingly, Dee himself did not actually use the mirror, and admitted that he'd never mastered the ability to scry; he left that to others who transmitted the messages to him. British Museum visitors may also see Dee's rose-tinted crystal, engraved gold and wax talisman tablets, wands and formula books.

In the later years of his life John Dee turned his ill directed attention to alchemy. Worse still, in 1582 he made the acquaintance of one Edward Kelley, a scoundrel who claimed mediumistic and magical abilities. That association was the downfall of the brilliant scholar, for at that point he abandoned all his truly useful and productive work to seek the ever elusive short cut to wealth and to divine wisdom. He soon found himself betrayed by Kelley and others who fed on what was left of his diminishing fame and repute. In 1583 a mob raided his home at Mortlake and destroyed many of his books, manuscripts, talismans and magical devices.

His last responsible position was as warden of the Collegiate Church in Manchester, where he was active during an infamous event known as 'The

Six'. In circumstances that were to be echoed by the case of the 'Devils of Loudun', in which a priest named Urbain Grandier was horribly tortured and burnt to death in 1634, and later by the 1692 Salem witch trials in the American colonies, a group of children in Manchester imagined themselves to be possessed by demons. What was then referred to as a 'cunning man' was brought in to observe and report on them. This poor man was caught up in the hysteria and was eventually executed on suspicion of being a witch himself. John Dee's only contribution was to advise the children to fast and pray. That was little comfort to the 'cunning man', whose cunning apparently deserted him when most needed.

On the death of Elizabeth in 1603, and the ascent to the throne of James I, who had no patience with anyone pretending to possess any sort of unorthodox magical powers, Dr Dee was stripped of his honours and his income and sent to live in the countryside incommunicado. He spent the last five years of his life in extreme poverty until his death in 1608 at the advanced age of eighty-one. His library of more than four thousand books on the occult, mathematics and cartography – the largest collection in Britain at that time – was dispersed soon after his death. He is buried at Mortlake.

The celebrated Mother Shipton

No reference to Mother Shipton prior to 1641 is in existence, so that what follows is not well supported by documents. It is even difficult to determine whether this English prophetess actually existed as she is represented in folklore, though writings seriously ascribed to her are being reproduced even today.

There were several women who claimed to be her: one lived in Oxfordshire near Wychwood Forest. But it is a Yorkshire claimant who has now won the title. From her we have much in print; nothing survives in writing from the others.

Mother Shipton is supposed to have been born in a cave at Dropping Well, Knaresborough, Yorkshire, in 1488, and the present town owes its tourist trade to that fact. She was Ursula Southill (or Sowthiel, or Southiel), the incredibly ugly daughter of Agatha Southill, known locally herself as a powerful witch. A biographer said in 1740,

'Her Stature was larger than common,
her Body crooked, her Face
frightful; but her Understanding extraordinary.'

Some time about 1512, a wealthy builder from York named Tobias Shipton married Ursula. One can only wonder why, unless she had unsuspected and unadvertised charms. Perhaps he was attracted by her extraordinary understanding.

Mother Shipton (Ursula Southill) was not a beauty, but her fame has persisted to this day.

She soon attained considerable notoriety throughout England as the 'Northern Prophetess' and, because of her dreadful appearance and reputed powers, was widely rumoured to be the child of Satan. The story is told that the Lord of the Underworld had met Ursula's mother in a field when she was only sixteen and promised her that if she would 'comply with his Desires' he would 'preserve her above the Reach of Want'. It is an offer many innocent young ladies have unwisely accepted, and we are told that Agatha 'readily condescended'. Alas, 'At length the Embraces of her infernal Gallant produced a pregnancy'. At the ensuing birth, 'such a terrible Storm of Thunder and Lightning appear'd, that Houses were beat down, Trees shatter'd, and the very Features of the Child were so warp'd and distorted, that it appear'd the very Master-Piece of Deformity.' It must have been a difficult delivery.

Mother Shipton's prognostications received great public attention, and were printed in pamphlets which were widely distributed. Though copies of these pamphlets and booklets still exist, most of what can be found today is sheer forgery, and many meteorological and astrological almanacs published as late as the nineteenth century used Mother Shipton's name freely. I have in my library a copy of an 1838 book which gives an idea of the overblown claims made for such tomes. It is titled:

THE
NEW UNIVERSAL
DREAM-BOOK;
OR THE
DREAMER'S SURE GUIDE
TO THE
Hidden Mysteries of Futurity:
TO WHICH ARE ADDED,
SEVERAL REMARKABLE DREAMS AND
UNDENIABLE PROOFS
OF THE
Real Importance of Interpreting Dreams.
By MOTHER SHIPTON.

I also have an 1870 reprint copy of a book of 1686 attributed to Edwin Pearson, *The Strange and Wonderful History of Mother Shipton*. Because of its similarity to another book, *Life and Death of Mother Shipton*, this biography was probably actually written by Richard Head, who also wrote *The English Rogue*, a racy account of his experiences with various tricksters, cheats and rascals of his day. Head himself was quite a renowned rascal.

Many local prophecies were invented and passed off under the Shipton name. In my library is a first edition of a book by John Tyrrel, *Past, Present and To Come: or, Mother Shipton's Yorkshire Prophecy*, published in 1740. In that volume is quoted what might well have been issued as a genuine prediction.

> Time shall happen A Ship shall sail upon the River *Thames*, till it reach the City of *London*, the Master shall weep, and cry out, Ah! What a flourishing City was this when I left it! Unequalled throughout the World! But now scarce a House is left to entertain us with a Flagon.

Obviously, this prophecy has all of recorded time in which to be fulfilled, for no date is given or even suggested. Since no cause of this calamity is specified, war, earthquake, fire or the advent of David Icke could all produce the cited effect. In fact no disaster of a physical nature is actually predicted. 'House' seems here to refer to a place of business that would be involved in providing a 'Flagon' to visiting sailors.

Regardless of all these problems, eager Shipton fans have declared that this is an accurate prophecy of the Great Fire of London which, as we've seen, is also said to have been foretold by Nostradamus, not to mention other seers. A perfect example of an unquestionably true Shipton 'prediction' is the often quoted and misquoted

> Eighteen hundred and thirty-five,
> Which of us shall be alive?
> Many a king shall end his reign,
> Many a knave his end shall gain.

Though one can hardly argue with this question and the two statements, the verse was resurrected at the end of 1934 with the change of one word. I dare say you can figure out which word it was.

The famous seeress died at the age of seventy-three in 1561, and is buried at Clifton, just outside the city of York. On her memorial is carved:

> Here lies she who never ly'd
> Whose skill so often has been try'd
> Her prophecies shall still survive
> And ever keep her name alive.

This is said to be the only such tribute to a witch in all of England, since the usual memorial, if any, is no more than a cairn of stones to mark the spot where such a person was hanged or burnt.

Endless refutations of Mother Shipton's rantings have done little or nothing to dampen enthusiasm among believers, who continue to pore over the verses seeking secrets of the future. Newly invented prophecies attributed to Mother Shipton continue to be published even today. Remember the rule: no amount of evidence against the phenomenon will convince the believer.

THE OLDEST HOAX IN HISTORY

The fault lies not in our stars,
but in ourselves.

CHAPTER 9

THE OLDEST HOAX IN HISTORY

He is a poor astrologer who pretends by the stars
to point out another's destiny, and yet does not know his own.
Ja'afar, AD 754-803

Astrology is the oldest form of claptrap ever to be foisted on the civilized world. In its beginnings, it was a genuine search for knowledge – an attempt to find, in the configurations of the stars and planets, some meaning for humans that might enable us to ascertain something about the future, as if that future were written, obscurely but gloriously, in the heavenly patterns that presented themselves to observers.

Such a notion is seductive. It makes things simpler by attributing to the stars everything from personal relationships to the destiny of nations. It eliminates the understandable confusion we feel as we face technology and specialized knowledge that are beyond our comprehension. It removes the need for personal responsibility and control, handing it all over to the mystics and to fate.

Today, though we now understand much of the true nature of the starry universe, there are among us individuals who still cling to the ancient notion that earthly events in the individual lives of each of us may be predicted from observations of the skies performed by experienced – perhaps inspired – practitioners of astrology.

This belief even extends into governmental offices, as in India, where astrology is taken quite seriously; and recently, to the great surprise and embarrassment of Americans, in the White House, where the First Lady was actually arranging the President's and her own official and personal schedules in accordance with the calculations of an astrologer retained by her for that purpose.

I have spoken to newspaper editors in the USA who assert that they can discontinue almost any feature in their publications and receive far fewer complaints than the avalanche of letters they would get if they dropped the astrology column. In spite of that economic fact, thirty-three papers in the USA and Canada, at the urging of the Committee for the Scientific Investigation of Claims of the Paranormal (CSICOP), now print at the head of their astrology piece: 'Horoscopes have no basis in scientific fact and

A client listens attentively to his astrologer in this medieval woodcut.

should be read for entertainment, not guidance.'

Now, I have said that I believe astrology to be 'claptrap'. That opinion is not based only on theoretical considerations, which alone must lead us to conclude that belief in astrology is irrational; no, my opinion is based upon much stronger evidence than that. I, and many other persons and organizations, have tested astrological claims time and time again, and this ancient belief has invariably failed to meet not only the practitioners' expectations, but any other simple test of the most basic effect.

Newspaper astrology — an early experiment

I find it incredible that 'Sun sign' astrology — the kind that is found in the newspaper columns — actually asks us to believe that, for one-twelfth of the entire population of the world, today is 'a good day to pursue new fashion ideas' or that another twelfth will find this a day to 'act boldly on property investments'. This applies whether you're a Maori lawyer, an Irish fisherman or a Peruvian geologist.

In 1946 a friend of mine in Montreal, Canada, started up a weekly tabloid newspaper which was at first intended as a satire on the flashy, cheap weeklies that were just then becoming available in that country. I offered to do an astrology column for the paper, as a test of what would be accepted by the average reader. The first issue proudly proclaimed that the internationally renowned astrologer Zo-Ran (for 'Zodiac-Randi') was writing exclusively for this new tabloid.

Trying to make it very obvious that the newspaper was satirical, the first issue had a front-page headline that promised, 'Nude adults of both sexes cavort in Dominion Square on Sunday! Exclusive photos in centerfold!' Those who eagerly turned to the centre saw just what was pledged, fully mature pigeons eating corn in Dominion Square.

To prepare my column I bought a regular astrology magazine, clipped out several pages of predictions, reduced them to individual phrases, and pasted those up in random order to form a sequence of twelve Sun sign predictions. For several weeks the column ran in the paper, and then the reaction began. Letters poured in for Zo-Ran, asking for personal horoscopes and other services. After the fifth week I'd proved my case and Zo-Ran bit the dust, never to be heard of again.

As this book goes to press, *Fate* Magazine, a US monthly equivalent of *Psychic News* — and every bit as dependable — has just revealed its startling discovery of my despicable past record as a 'fake astrologer' — which was actually described long ago in my 1982 book, *Flim-Flam!*, now in its tenth printing. Incredibly, *Fate* offered me space in their magazine to apologize for my past transgression!

Jonathan Cainer is an astrologer who produces a daily column for several British newspapers. He agreed to take part in our programme. We gave him

accurate birth information for two unnamed studio guests and asked him to cast horoscopes for them, which he did before he appeared in front of our cameras. He read out the readings he'd prepared, and then we introduced the two subjects, Stephen Fry and Hugh Laurie. Their opinions of the readings were that they were general in nature, and not at all helpful. In fact, Hugh made an impassioned attack on what he referred to as the 'nonsense' that seemed harmless but was in reality damaging to those who were taken in by it, in that it removed their personal responsibility for their own acts and made them dependent on seers and crystal gazers.

Stephen Fry echoed his colleague's opinion, and later, writing in his 'Fry on Friday' column in the *Daily Telegraph*, he amplified his views:

> The human mind, after all, is remarkable enough in its ability to write symphonies, build suspension bridges, invent a thousand types of corkscrew, predict to the minute the appearance of comets in the sky and devise new daytime television game-show formats, without us having to pretend it has unprovable, unknowable and untestable powers to receive spirit messages from Red Indians or read character from birth-dates as well. . . . Superstition is not just harmless fun. It is, in fact, bad luck to be superstitious, for the simple reason that in this world it is bad luck to be foolish.

Testing the untestable

The only way to test astrology properly, without depending on endless anecdotal and largely unprovable evidence along with wild pseudoscientific theories, is to ask the astrologers what they can do, and with what accuracy, and to then test their claims in a fair, mutually agreed fashion. We did not content ourselves with a trial of simple newspaper astrology. To be fair, we had to have some 'proper' horoscopes cast.

For the first of the *James Randi: Psychic Investigator* programmes, we had in our audience two persons who gave us the date, time and place of their birth. These three elements, astrologers tell us, can provide the information needed for accurate horoscopes, which are charts of the positions of the heavens above that spot at that moment – positions which, they say, indicate important data. We felt that an astrologer should be able to produce significant results for them.

Enter the expert

An astrologer named **Tad Mann** used modern technology to generate the data he believed necessary to determine certain facts about these two persons, and was able to examine this data for 48 hours. Mr Mann's claim is that he can pick out specific dates in the subjects' lives and tell what happened at those times. He then produced 30-minute readings on audio cassettes, which we gave to the subjects, Jilly Cooper and Nina Myskow. When he prepared these readings, Mann knew only that the subjects were women, but we told him exactly who they were just before he read out shorter versions for them on camera, prefacing it all with a comment that it was difficult to do this in 20 seconds. (In fact the readings were quite a bit longer at 78 and 87 seconds respectively.)

I will return to what he read out in a moment, but first I should like to say a few things about his philosophy and methods.

Hunt the analogy

Ever since I heard that the Maharishi Mahesh Yogi of Transcendental Meditation fame has a doctorate in physics, I've been very wary of scientists who have lots of education but aren't very scientific. This yogic person, in common with most amateur philosophers, gropes about for a simple analogy to demonstrate a novel notion, failing to recognize that analogies are only for purposes of illustration and simplification, and do not often represent parallels. The Maharishi actually equates the solar system, with its planets orbiting about central Sun, with the atom and its accompanying electrons orbiting a central nucleus. It doesn't take much science to recognize that not only is His Holiness thereby ignorant of the actual state of the atom, but that his parallel is ludicrous.

There is an important difference between pseudoscience and crackpot science. The former has some of the trappings, generally the appearance and much of the language used by real science, while the latter has no pretensions at all of appearing to be science. The present German fascination with imaginary 'E-rays' and the tiresome speculations on how dowsing is supposed to work are both pseudoscience; most perpetual motion ideas and things like reflexology, palmistry and psychometry are crackpot. The Maharishi's solar system-atom analogy is not only crackpot, it is very bad crackpot.

The 'Cylinder of Life'

The 'theory' that Tad Mann proposes assumes a great deal, gives unsupported definitions and states conclusions that are unproven and untested. It is classic crackpot, but sounds just great to the uninformed because of the language, which almost brings it into the slightly more respectable classification of pseudoscience. On our programme, Mr Mann told us about it. He said:

> The astrological birth horoscope is a map, a symbolic representation of your lifetime from conception to death. Astrology is a language for describing a very perceptive view of your life, its events and relationships, and your underlying psychology. But how does astrology work?

Twelve years ago I proposed an intriguing hypothesis to explain astrology. The Sun moves through space at thousands of kilometres per day and the paths of the planets make spiral patterns around the Sun's central filament. A birth horoscope is a slice through this spiralling circus seen at a particular moment in time from a place on Earth.

The spiralling form of the solar system is similar in structure to the genetic molecule DNA, which determines form and behaviour of every living cell. Through the phenomenon of resonance, information is thus transmitted to every being on Earth. This explains the ancient mystical axiom, 'As above, so below.' Astrology is an attempt to interpret the language of the cosmos as it affects our lives.

When we are well integrated, we respond to natural rhythms and our life works. When we are out of touch with the cosmos, we become ill and our lives do not work. Astrology is a language for regaining contact with the world around us.

Because planetary cycles are repetitive, it is possible to describe events both in the past and in the future. The Cylinder of Life allows the astrologer to describe a person's development through gestation, childhood and maturity.

The signs of the zodiac describe the qualities and character of the process. The planets signify the people in our life, our own behavioural archetypes and the organs and glands which affect our psychological and physiological behaviour.

Astrology provides a wonderful tool for understanding why we do what we do and how we can begin to accept and work with ourselves in this troubled world. It also gives us a glimpse of the spiritual potential of being human.

Please note that Tad Mann has invented special terminology here ('Sun's central filament'), promises relief from 'this troubled world', and assures us that we are clearly represented in the heavens, even down to our friends and our 'organs and glands'. I have found this kind of quasi-religious ranting to be typical of such offerings. His statement that the paths of the Sun and planets provide a figure which is 'similar in structure to the genetic molecule DNA' is just not true at all. Then, denying the effects of bacteria, bullets, floods, old age and muggers, he even claims that if we are 'out of touch with the cosmos, we become ill', another assertion without any shred of evidence at all to support it.

Though we had introduced Mr Mann to our TV audience as a 'scientist and astrologer' it turned out that he had credentials only as an architect, having earned a bachelor's degree in architecture from Cornell University. That is hardly my definition of a scientist, and may explain why this gentleman apparently has such a poor grasp of scientific method.

A resounding spiral

First, and as his contracted requirement for his appearance on the programme, Tad Mann was allowed to lecture the audience, giving the above summary of his highly individual method of looking at the world. His actual theory involves the spirals that the planets describe in space, if we assume that the solar system is moving somewhere in a direction at right angles to the general plane of the system. This set of spirals is supposed to have a resonant relationship with the DNA structure of living matter. (Please bear in mind that I am only describing this bizarre theory, not endorsing it.)

Mann evidently has an idea that the solar system is moving at a given speed through space ('thousands of kilometres a day') but fails to say what that speed is relative to. So that I may explain this serious discrepancy, please consider this scenario. Time is speeded up, and you are standing still in a spaceship, just 'above' (which of course has no meaning here either, but stay with me for a moment) the solar system, spread out 'below' in all its majesty. It appears to be hovering in space, while the individual planets revolve about the Sun. But there are no 'spirals' here from our point of view, only the ellipses in which those planets move. Mann says that the spirals are generated because as the ellipses are being generated, they are also moving in line with the 'Sun's central filament', whatever that may be. But I said our spaceship is standing still, watching the system 'below' us. And if it is stationary relative to the system (or relative to the Sun, if you wish), it must be moving at the same speed and in the same direction as the solar system, just to stay in that relationship. And it really is moving, relative to whichever of the billions of other stars he cares to choose – but how is that choice made? Choose any one of a vast multitude of them, and the system is moving much faster, much slower, forwards, backwards or sideways!

I believe that Tad Mann has reached through the looking-glass rather than out into space to come up with what I feel to be a quite inconsistent and an unrelated configuration and process involving the cosmos, all to force astrology into another mystical picture. No similarity exists between the two 'spirals', one major reason being that the larger one is a path in space generated over time, and the smaller is an actual physical configuration of molecules. I suggest that there is a far better correlation – and resonance – between the coil springs in my car and my DNA than there is in the Mann theory.

The two readings

Tad Mann's short versions of his readings for Jilly Cooper and Nina Myskow follow. The words in brackets are those that were left out from Mr Mann's script when he read it on TV, and the italicized words are those he said. By the time he was reading these before the camera, he had learned who the ladies were that his readings were intended for, something he had not known when preparing them earlier.

For Jilly Cooper

You are extremely powerful emotionally, yet underneath it all you may feel [very] *quite* vulnerable. I feel you have a keen interest in *fantasy* and drama.

[July and December] 1969 was a [negative] *difficult and uncertain* time which could have seen a separation of some kind.

[In] 1976 you came into contact with someone intensely powerful [but the relationship] *who* didn't *quite* live up to *your* expectations.

In 1979 you underwent a major change in appearance – [you] *and* also began new and very strong relationships.

1982-1984 was *quite* a difficult time.

But 1989 was perhaps the most traumatic period in your adult life. It may have been the end of a long-standing relationship but at the same time some new and positive elements started to appear in your life which may still be in operation now.

This year, 1991, is *going to be* a great one for you. You will receive and deserve an extraordinary degree of recognition. You may now feel the desire to uproot yourself and seek out a new set of challenges *in a totally different direction.*

For Nina Myskow

You are well balanced and diplomatic as long as you get your own way. An attractive lady, you enjoy food and other people's attention. You have great need for love and if it isn't shown there's a tendency to go into a sulk or have a fit of temper.

1963 was a focus point, you wanted to be [seen] *noticed* by other people [and] *but* weren't *to the degree that you wanted to be.* 1965 brought an influential man into your life but in November 1969 you underwent a profound change and adopted a public persona, a mask you will identify with more and more as you grow older.

By [June] 1972 you received an enormous amount of public recognition and became much more outspoken. November 1979 was extremely significant and represents a relationship, possibly the [birth of children and] desire to have a family.

From '83 [, '84 and] *to* '85 seem to be good years but with dramatic

changes in direction *and a desire for greater stability and security.*
However, it is August 1990 that brings a sudden skyrocketing
change, with success and possible awards. The next three years [may]
will see a complete change in profession and greater self expression
*more in line with your ideals that you have been creating for many
years.*

I ask you to look back to the first sentence in each of these readings. The
generality and universal application of the guesses is very evident. In the
remainder of the readings, the dropped-in modifiers, dropped-out months
and other changes show how much the readings were changed once Tad
Mann knew who the subjects were. As provisional words and phrases used
here, we find: 'could have', 'I feel', 'may' (6 times), 'of some kind',
'perhaps', 'possibly', 'a tendency to', and 'seem to be'.

In the improved version 'July 1969' and 'December 1969' became simply
'1969'. 'June 1972' was suddenly just '1972'. The increase in latitude there
is obvious: for each of the three dates, there is now twelve times as much
chance of success.

Confusion

Jilly Cooper and Nina Myskow responded to Tad Mann's readings in a most
interesting fashion. Like most people faced with such a situation, they
recognized their responsibility to try to make the facts fit the fantasy.

Jilly failed to make Tad's call of 1969 as a 'difficult and uncertain time'
fit in (he had originally called it a 'negative' year, but changed his mind as
he was reading his script) because it was a very good year, when she got her
really big break. Mann had called for her to undergo 'a major change in
appearance' and to begin 'new and very strong relationships' in 1979, but
though neither happened, she thought that the fact a 'good book' of hers
came out that year, was close enough to the prophecy to fit.

Mann called for 1989 to be 'perhaps the most traumatic period in [her]
adult life. It may have been the end of a long-standing relationship but at
the same time some new and positive elements started to appear in [her]
life.' In the altered version he read on the show, Mann added to the end of
that prediction the phrase 'which may still be in operation now'. This means
of spreading the prophecy a little wider goes along well with the 'perhaps'
and the 'may have been' to blur an already vague statement, adding yet
another 'may' to it. Under prompting by Tad Mann, all Jilly agreed with for
1989 was that it 'wasn't a brilliant year'. Faint praise.

But Nina was simply ecstatic. 'I have to say I was staggered by how
accurate he was,' she said after she had listened to the full 30-minute
recorded reading Tad Mann had given her. I believe from an analysis of the
reading that Ms Myskow is easily staggered. Mann had failed to mention a

nervous breakdown she had in May 1979, but had said that November of that year 'represents a relationship, possibly the desire to have a family'. Note the use of the modifier 'possibly' again, and that in his spoken version he chose to omit a phrase describing November that he'd used in the written version, namely, 'the birth of children'. But remember that by the time he was reading the script he was aware of whom the prediction was meant for. Nina had no children in that year, nor in any other of the twelve years since. She chose to accept the bare 'relationship' that Mann mentioned, because that was the year she met her therapist, which she said was the 'most significant relationship in [her] adult life'. Notice that the 'birth of children and desire to have a family' were forgotten, because they missed. In this game, we're only looking for successes; we ignore failures in the reading.

Now look back at what Mr Mann conjured up for Nina in 1965. That's the year Mann said would bring 'an influential man into [her] life'. Could Nina have confused the years 1965 and 1975 in accepting this bit?

In another classic response, Nina Myskow recalled that Tad Mann had called for a time between the ages of eight and fifteen when she would have a 'rebellion with [her] father'. Ms Myskow acknowledged to our audience that, while 'every child may have conflicts with their fathers [*sic*]', this very much applied to her. Actually, the fact is that she was separated from her father at eight, when she moved with her mother from Scotland to South Africa, and he died when she was twelve! That in no way matches the 'rebellion' requirement, but in this game it can be forced in because the word 'father' was used, and it jams into place easily enough.

Finally, Nina told Mann that she didn't get the exciting 'skyrocketing change, with success and possible awards' in August 1990 that he had clearly forecast, but that year she did meet the man of her life, and she accepted that. Again, that event was supposed to be back in 1965, but twenty-five years isn't too far off, in this business. And there's our old friend 'possible' being popped in again, just in case the statement was too specific.

Well, the past wasn't too accurate, but let's wait and see how the Cylinder of Life manages to predict the future for both Jilly and Nina. If they don't go off in a 'totally different direction' in 1991 or make a 'complete change in profession' in the next three years, we'll have further reason to doubt the worth of Tad Mann's method.

Some devastating opinions

Dr Alan Chapman, historian, scientist and fellow of the Royal Astronomical Society, was present when Tad Mann gave us his startling theory. I asked him what he thought of it. He said to Mann:

Frankly, nothing whatsoever. I think it's a load of rubbish . . . you're using an ancient cosmology, in other words a cosmology that was quite reputable until the seventeenth century and then you're simply forgetting that it was blown to bits between about 1650 and 1700. You're forgetting that the corpse was ever killed. You are resurrecting bits of the limbs and you're creating a sort of a sociological version of Frankenstein's monster. . . . It's not just a bit of fun, it's not just amusing, it's not just 'Oh, well, there no harm in it, is there?' I think it's an insult to the human spirit, this species of bullshit, and I think we should be angry about it. . . . It's not perhaps as bad as spiritualist mediums, but it covers the same ground, the poor bewildered people who are told by the astrologer that somehow they're important and extraordinary because the whole universe was poised in a unique state just at the moment of their birth. . . . Now, people are special and different. They are unique, but the human spirit is not represented by this kind of determinant nonsense.

I asked Dr John Maddox, editor of *Nature* magazine, for his opinion of astrology. As the one who accepts or rejects articles for this leading science journal, he has received articles on every sort of pseudoscience and nonsense that can be imagined. He shared with us his reaction to a paper he published that was sent in by Shawn Carlson, an American physicist.

. . . one of the things we have published on astrology a few years back was a very carefully done study in California with the collaboration of twenty-eight astrologers from the San Francisco area and lots of subjects – 118 of them altogether – and lunar charts were made by the astrologers. It turned out that the people couldn't recognize their own charts any more accurately than by chance . . . and that seems to me to be a perfectly convincing and lasting demonstration of how well this thing works in practice. My regret is that there's so many intelligent, able people wasting their time and, might I say, taking other people's money in this hopeless cause.

How not to play the market

We regularly hear of astrologers who work for major companies and individuals as financial advisors. I've found that the accounts given of success in this work are usually highly inflated, and on *James Randi: Psychic Investigator* I was interested in testing such a claim. An eligible astrologer named Roy Gillet was accepted on the basis of his assertions that he had calculated horoscopes and used them to give advice on financial moves to satisfied customers through his organization, Roy Gillet Consultants. John Piper, a trader and technical analyst, appeared opposite Mr Gillet.

Under the supervision of Mr Tracy Moreshead, marketing director of financial dealers IG Index, £10,000 was (theoretically) given to Roy and an equal sum to John. They were to invest it according to their respective specialities for a period of five weeks, ending in March 1991, appropriately on Budget Day. Then all three participants appeared on our programme and we announced the results.

John Piper, using recognized market skills during the very volatile period of the Gulf War, showed a profit of just under £1,800, while Roy Gillet, using astrology, ended up with a loss of more than £4,000. After the programme Roy lamented that he had lost £3,000 in one move alone, which he said was a 'hunch' bet. I reminded him that he had been asked to test astrology, not hunches and, had his astrology scored a success on this short test, I'm sure that he would gladly have claimed a win.

As with all our tests, this one was of limited value because it just did not have enough data to establish whether or not financial astrology works. I would very much like to test this – and all the other subjects we handled – in greater depth.

Statistics in an astrology test

In my US programme *Exploring Psychic Powers: Live!* the astrologer we tested agreed to match twelve persons, each with a different astrological sign, to the correct sign just by asking them questions, observing their characteristics and noting other personality traits. We required only ten to be correctly matched, but he was confident he could match all twelve. Unless astrology really worked his chances of success were quite small. But if astrology works at all, he certainly should have been able to accomplish this simple task.

Statistics are not always easy to understand. We can all recognize that the chances of a head or a tail showing up when a coin is flipped must be exactly 50 per cent – if the coin and the throw are fair, of course. If we observe a good number of flips (at least several hundred) we will find that the 50 per cent expectation is quite well met. In fact, with a very large number of flips, it will probably be met almost exactly.

But suppose that we have a more complicated experimental set-up, such as that accepted by our astrologer in the American test. We had agreed that he must obtain a minimum match of ten persons out of the twelve to their respective signs, in order to meet our challenge and walk away with the prize money. But please note that any number of hits above five would have appeared significant.

How likely is the astrologer merely to guess the correct match for ten signs out of twelve? The odds for this are one in many millions, a truly astronomical (rather than astrological) figure. However, we must look at it this way: the chances of a man falling out of a train window by accident are very slim; yet if that man is trying to get out the window, his chances of success are excellent! In the case of the astrological test we were conducting, our astrologer was using a technique which he and many other persons believe has an old and respected history. Chance should not have entered into it at all.

Two months before our British test, seized by a sudden experimental urge to discover what I myself could do by sheer chance, I numbered a dozen ping-pong balls from one to twelve, prepared an egg carton by numbering each compartment, and threw the balls randomly into the carton 100 times. From this admittedly limited experiment I found that by chance alone I was able to obtain zero correct matches 40 per cent of the time, one correct match 36 per cent of the time, and two, three or four matches each 23 per cent. These experimental results are very close to the mathematically calculated probability. On only one trial did six balls fall into their correct places; the odds against this are more than 10,000 to one. So, even if I'd had only this sketchy experimental evidence as a basis, if chance alone were operating in this test I'd have expected that the astrologer would have either one or none correct. To save time in our US test, we had given our astrologer an opportunity to conduct his survey of the twelve subjects earlier in the day, and had videotaped the process. Of course, he was not allowed to ask the subjects when they had been born, since that would immediately give away their signs. But he was allowed great latitude with the other questions.

A change of expression

After the astrologer had made his decision, our twelve subjects were each given a sealed envelope containing his decision on their birth sign. Then came the moment of truth before the live cameras. First I asked him if he was quite satisfied with the conditions of the test. He said that he was. There were twelve positions marked out on the studio floor, each with a star sign. We instructed the subjects to open their envelopes and to go to the sign thus indicated. They did. Next they were told that if their actual birth sign was different from the one they were now standing at, they were to step forward and go to the correct one. Remember, chance alone would result in either none or one of the matches being correct.

Fortunately, the astrologer's face was not showing at this moment, for all twelve subjects stepped forward! I was watching. His jaw dropped, and he staggered slightly. But, to his great credit, he offered no excuses or accusations then or after the programme.

The British test

When we made *James Randi: Psychic Investigator*, we had a hard time finding an astrologer who would agree to a trial like that described above.

Two at first said they'd have a go at it, then they had second thoughts. However, a lady named Carole Golder finally agreed to be tested in a less demanding way. Carole had predicted in 1984 that Prince Charles and Princess Diana would have a 'large family', and that a portentous event – which she did not deny sounded like a coronation – would take place in 1987. Carole agreed to a relatively light-hearted matching trial, in which we would see if happily married couples were actually mated in accordance with the way astrology might pair them off. With some difficulty we managed to find twelve couples in which were represented, on the male side, all twelve zodiacal signs.

Carole agreed to ask the signs of all the women (which were not necessarily all different), and she would advise them on which men they should be mated to, according to her art. On the programme the couples marched out in their correct pairing, then the women were asked to join the men with whom astrology said they should be.

To our amusement, one of the men got three wives this way, one of them got two and one got back his own along with two new ones. Only one couple remained matched as they had been.

Was this a definitive and conclusive test? Of course not. Carole Golder was a good sport to have tried it, and we appreciated her willingness to participate. She had said in advance that she didn't expect great success, but one wonders whether astrology fans expected this experiment to show positive results.

A final word on astrology

I will admit that astrology does have one real benefit: it enables us to determine at least one character trait in human beings. Watch for those who read their Sun sign predictions in the daily newspapers, and you will know that those folks are silly. But of course, the main reason I don't believe in astrology is that I'm a Sagittarius, and we're known to be very hard to convince of such things.

EPILOGUE

EPILOGUE

*Madness is consistent; which is more than can be
said for poor reason. Whatever may be
the ruling passion at the time continues equally
so throughout the whole delirium, though
it should last for life.*
Laurence Sterne, 1713-1768

It stands to reason that the people who agreed to appear on our show to be tested very likely believed in their own powers. There may have been some exceptions to that observation; but if so, I think that any insincere claimants found few loopholes in our experimental design, and they might thus have been at a disadvantage. We cannot claim that we were perfect in this regard, some concessions having been made in the interests of better viewing; but we tried to assure that spurious claims would have a difficult time surviving our procedures.

I must say that if an experienced conjuror had been subjected to our tests, he or she would have had little problem getting around the security procedures, but we had to assume that no conjurors had applied!

It must not be assumed that those who failed to obtain their expected results were or are in any way dishonest or that they purposely misrepresented themselves. They may have been mistaken, but that's a fault we all must admit to, from time to time; an honest mistake is neither a sin nor a crime. If it were, I myself would certainly be doomed to perdition – or behind bars – at this moment. Come to think of it, I'm not at all sure about the first of those.

I hope that the claimants who appeared on these programmes will continue to think kindly of us, whether or not they were successful in establishing their claims. We – and I speak for the entire staff of our programme – were most grateful for their participation. We respect them and we value their participation, without which our audience would have had to suffer through my endless parlour tricks. Even my mother tired of those.

We began our quest with the intention of discovering whether or not certain persons can actually look into the future, heal by their touch, cause objects to move by mind power, read character, discover water or treasure by means of forked sticks, forecast events by observing the stars, or speak with the voices of the dead. It was for me, as usual, a fascinating inquiry.

We confidently expected to receive a lot of comments, pro and con, concerning our six programmes. Some of those comments would be useful, and all of them would be interesting. My experience has been that a few viewers would express doubts that 'science', as such, can resolve whether or not psychic powers actually exist. Science designs experiments to test ideas and theories; and, most importantly, science is prepared to change its conclusions if better or different evidence is presented. In that last respect it differs radically from religion, superstition and crackpot or pseudoscientific notions.

Now, it is widely assumed by less experienced sceptical observers of these subjects that those who believe in psychic powers are strangely dressed gnome-like creatures who wear wire pyramids on their heads, are festooned with crystals and eat food that resembles discarded packing material. Not so. Though such people certainly do exist in the ranks of the believers, most of those who at least tentatively accept claims of psychic events are quite ordinary persons who in many cases have not been informed of the methods by which such unusual claims must be examined. Our programme was meant as a first step in informing them, as well as a step in the seemingly endless examination of mystical powers.

Science can determine the reality of these claims, fairly and definitively. The facts are there to be found, regardless of what any of us might want those facts to be. All of us who worked on *James Randi: Psychic Investigator* were interested to see, if our claimants failed to prove their case on these programmes, what excuses they would offer to, or be offered by, some sections of the press. Certainly, loud cries of 'negative vibrations', 'sceptic' and 'unbeliever' would be heard, but we expected very few legitimate objections. We went to much trouble to ensure that our audience would have good reason to accept that our procedures were fairly and properly implemented.

At every step we asked that competent independent authorities be brought in to approve the agenda, and only after such approval was obtained did we proceed. Those who offered their claims were required to approve the procedures before we went ahead, and they all did so. More than one test had to be dropped because such agreement could not be reached. Most of those who responded to our requests for claimants tried to plan the show their way without any regard for proper conduct of an experiment; these persons were not asked to become further involved.

Those who were debarred from participation will, I'm sure, never tire of offering a multitude of rationalizations for their exclusion. The facts are simple: they were not willing to be properly tested, and they backed out when confronted with a genuine test. I ask you to remember that most of these persons were professional psychics who charge for their services and support themselves by this means. It is significant to me that they refused to be genuinely tested, when all they had to do was to demonstrate what they do every day, but under proper observing conditions. Would you buy tomatoes from a grocer who refused to show you the tomatoes before you paid for them? A customer is even entitled to squeeze a tomato gently. We didn't put any pressure on our subjects.

We stepped through the looking-glass in pursuit of strange forces, and they were not there.

APPENDIX:

An offer

AN OFFER

This statement outlines the general rules covering my offer concerning psychic, supernatural or paranormal claims. Since claims will vary greatly in character and scope, specific rules must be formulated for each claimant. However, all claimants must agree to the rules set forth here before any formal agreement is entered into. A claimant will declare agreement by signing this form where indicated before a solicitor, commissioner for oaths or notary public and returning the form to me. The eventual test procedure must be agreed upon by both parties before any testing procedures will take place. I shall not act as a judge. Nor shall I design the protocol independently of the claimant. All claimants must identify themselves properly before any discussion takes place. Owing to the large amount of correspondence exchanged on this subject, all correspondence must include a stamped, self-addressed envelope.

I, James Randi, will pay the sum of US$10,000 to any person or persons who will demonstrate any psychic, supernatural or paranormal ability of any kind under satisfactory observing conditions. Such demonstration must take place under these rules and limitations:

1 The claimant must state clearly in advance, and the claimant and Mr Randi will agree upon, what powers or abilities will be demonstrated, the limits of the proposed demonstration (as far as time, location and other variables are concerned) and what will constitute both a positive and a negative result.

2 Only an actual performance of the stated nature and scope within the agreed limits is acceptable.

3 The claimant agrees that all data of any kind (photographic, recorded, written or other) gathered as a result of the testing may be used freely by me in any way I choose.

4 Tests will be designed in such a way that no judging procedure is required. Results will be self-evident to any observer, in accordance with the rules which will be agreed upon by all parties in advance of any formal testing procedure taking place. No part of the testing procedure may be changed in any way without the express agreement of all parties concerned.

5 I may ask the claimant to perform informally before an appointed representative, if distance and time dictate that need, for purposes of determining whether the claimant is likely to perform as promised.

6 I will not pay for expenses incurred by the claimant, such as transportation, accommodation or other costs.

7 When entering into this challenge, claimant surrenders any and all rights to legal action against me, as far as this may be done by established statutes. This applies to injury, accident or any other damage of a physical or emotional nature and/or financial or professional loss of any kind.

8 Prior to the commencement of the formal testing procedure, I will give my cheque for the full reward amount into the keeping of an independent person chosen by the claimant. In the event that the claimant is successful under the agreed terms and conditions, that cheque for US$10,000 shall be immediately surrendered to the claimant by the person holding that cheque, in full settlement.

9 Copies of this document are available free of charge to any person who requests it and sends the required stamped, self-addressed envelope to me.

10 This offer is made by me personally, and not on behalf of any other person, agency or organization, though others may become involved in the examination of claims, and others may add their reward money to mine in certain circumstances.

11 This offer is open to any and all persons, in any part of the world, regardless of sex, race, educational background or other characteristics, and will continue in effect until the prize is awarded, or until my death. My legal will states that, upon my death, the reward amount will be held in escrow and in charge of the Committee for Scientific Investigation of Claims of the Paranormal, in Buffalo, New York, which is then empowered to continue the offer for a period of ten years after my demise, after which the reward amount can be used by them for whatever purpose they desire.

12 THE CLAIMANT MUST AGREE UPON WHAT WILL CONSTI-
TUTE A CONCLUSION THAT HE OR SHE DOES NOT POSSESS
THE CLAIMED ABILITY OR POWER. This rule must be accepted
by the claimant without reservation.

The claimant, by signing, notarizing and returning this form, signifies
agreement with the above rules.

James Randi
12000 NW 8th Street
Plantation, FL 33325-1406
USA   Claimant's signature

INDEX

Picture Acknowledgements

The publishers and author would like to thank the following sources for the use of the photographs on the pages listed:

Frontispiece Mary Evans Picture Library

page

32	James Randi
33	James Randi
35	James Randi
38	James Randi
55	James Randi
56	James Randi
57	Mary Evans Picture Library
59	Mary Evans Picture Library
64	James Randi
65	James Randi
66	James Randi
73	James Randi
75	Mary Evans Picture Library
78	Granada Television/Stewart Darby
93	*Sunday People*/John Frost Newspapers
97	Mary Evans Picture Library
98	Mary Evans Picture Library
107	Granada Television/Stewart Darby
113	James Randi
118	James Randi
120	James Randi
128	James Randi
130	Granada Television/Stewart Darby